# CAT TALES

## DEDICATED TO ALL CATS KNOWN AND IMAGINED

For Kitty

Love,

Mary

ISBN: 1537394045

Printed by CreateSpace, An Amazon.com Company

# Contributors

Writers
  Polly Brewer
  Toni Eames
  Julie Harcos
  Juliana Harris
  J. H. Livingston
  Richard Stone

Illustrators & Photographers
  Avigdar Adams, Photographer
  John Barnard, Artist • johnbarnardart.com
  J. H. Livingston, Writer & Artist
  Benjamin Locke, Artist • fresnoarts.net/profile/BenjaminFranklinLocke
  Steve Norton, Artist • Images from Catnap by Steve Norton ©2015 • stevenorton.com
  Irven Rule, Photographer
  Timothy Savage, Photographer

Cover Art
  Karen Kozlow, Artist • karenkozlow.fanfairepromotions.com

# Table of Contents

# Table of Contents

# Foreword

Steve Norton

# Why Cats?

by Richard Stone

Another book about cats? Suddenly the world, especially cyberspace, seems full of cats: cats cute and cats ferocious; cats at play or in gravest repose; cats musical and cats dramatic. So why more cats? Simply, it's because we, the fabricators of this collection, have cats-in-our-lives as a common denominator. As writers (three of us are in fact part of an on-going writing group) who often deal in memoir, we have in due course documented our cats as an important part of our lives. Also, gathering and composing new pieces has been a natural and congenial way to collaborate. It has been absorbing and stimulating to hear and critique each other's very different pieces.

In addition to the work of our group members (Polly, Richard and Juliana), we invited a few feline-fancying friends to contribute to the collection, and we solicited illustrations and photos from artists of our acquaintance. We hope this makes for a unique collection, moving as it does from flights of fancy to starkest reality, from observations of mundane routine to epic narrative.

In the end, this book exists primarily as a shared endeavor based on our experiences with these strange and wonderful beings who provide a gateway into a world otherwise beyond our knowing. If a significant part of religious practice is a humbling of the ego, it is no wonder that cats have been the subject of devotion for centuries. To paraphrase another admirer, "To have a cat in your life is to accept the reality that you are not all-important."

# Counterpoint

Avigdar Adams

# Cat Credo: What I Believe About Cats

by Richard Stone

Cats as I know them (unlike dogs) act from an awareness where humans only peripherally exist and then mainly as providers of food, entertainment and comfort.

Some cats are kindly disposed toward us, and enjoy our company. Others know how to engage us when convenient, but don't miss us when we're gone.

Cats can read our minds ... or at least sense our intentions. They know which chair we're going to sit in and get there before we even move. Before we can be seen, they know when we're coming with the medicine.

Cats are private, they don't want us to know their business. They act independent of our preferences. One of my cats disappeared for three days, and as he had lost a lot of weight recently I thought he might have died. The fourth morning I woke up to find him sleeping by my side.

Cats have an ancient lineage and most feel secure or at least entitled to security. Those that don't (I have one such) will seek out a territory where they feel safe most of the time.

Cats live both within and beyond our world. They mystify us, and we enjoy it. And they know it. And use it.

All cats walk in beauty, even the funny-looking ones.

Cats allow us safely to re-experience our hunter/predator ancestry. Through them we can recall the focus, patience and persistence our species once needed for survival, and which our problem-solving abilities still rest on. Cats amplify and complicate our sense of self.

It is a real question who is whose pet.

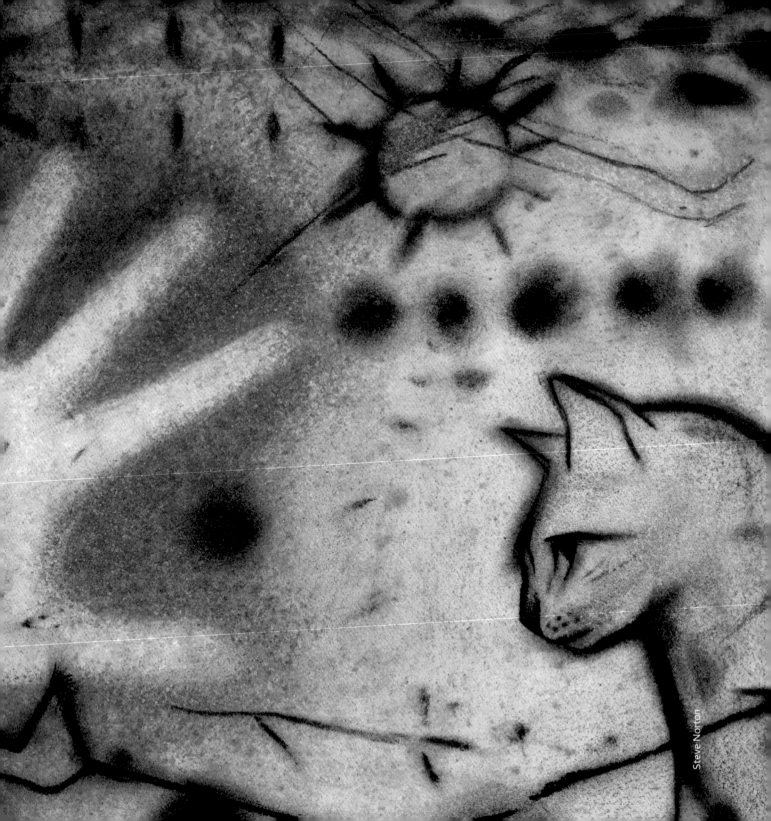

Steve Norton

# Cats and Humans

## by Polly Brewer

Outside of distracting and amusing ourselves during the hot Fresno summer, why are we writing about cats?

I think it is because they offer us so many anomalies and contradictions, so much outpouring of spirits and inventiveness, fascinating to watch and share.

It seems to me that Richard is saying that cats use us humans as convenient food providers, door openers, warm laps only when needed.

I think there are far more intense relationships going on between us and the cats. I do know, in my long life, I have seldom been without cats and, on those occasions when they could not be present, I have missed them enormously—longed for their comfort, craved for interactions with them. One year for several months I had no cats. A big one who lived nearby seemed to sense very clearly my language. I would call him as I passed his house, feeling a bit foolish because I had found out that his name was Sunshine and it seemed odd to call that out on an empty street, but he always bounded toward me so quickly that I had a sense he had been waiting, watching for me to pass. He always offered himself so willingly for stroking. I felt he was giving friendship, not as a pleasant distraction for him, but because he also had a sure sense of my need.

I have felt these intensities many times in other ways. Take, for instance, the blissful, inward cat smiles in reaction to my petting and scratching their sinuous bodies under the sleek fur that is so soothing to me. I always feel that my human needs and theirs have interacted intensely as we have both entered each other's world.

# Cats and Me

by Juliana Harris

Polly and Richard have well described the cat's mystique and natural ability to sense human mood and offer an appropriate response. I had a lonely childhood and might have had a problem with imaginary playmates had I not been surrounded by scores of Siamese cats and kittens. They were my best friends. I talked to them and they talked back, which is how I became fluent in pure Siamese.

Unusual circumstances led my mother into the Siamese trade. One Thanksgiving, my brother came home from boarding school with three Thai princes in tow. Bringing foreign friends home for the holidays was common of boarding students. I was too young to remember the teenaged princes, but I will never forget the extraordinary gifts they gave my parents–three purebred Siamese kittens. My mother named the kittens after the boys: Adoul, Taiwee and Verischatti. Eventually, when the adult females gave birth within days of each other, they stole one another's kittens and hid them in remote places. Missing kittens sent the mothers into frenzied states of mournful wails, panicked shrieks and deathly howls, as only the Siamese can do. My mother and the handyman pressed their ears to the walls to determine from where the faint mews came. Off flew panels of knotty pine and insulation. Inside the heating ducts, behind recessed pipes, beneath the furnace, in between the rafters–kittens everywhere–a testament to the resourcefulness of their Siamese mothers.

I delighted in these gorgeous creatures, forcing the kittens into doll clothes, doll carriages, doll beds and doll houses. As I grew older, cats nestled into the crook of my elbow while I read Nancy Drew and the Hardy Boys. Later, they moved into Barbie and Ken's world but could not fit into their clothes. In my teen years, they sprawled upon my homework and basked in the heat of my desk lamp. It was not until I went away to college that I learned to spend the night without a cat beneath the covers. For all these reasons, I have no objectivity about the subject of cats, and contributing to a book of cat tales is pure delight!

# Remembrances of Cats Past

Timothy Savage

# The Kingly Cat

by Polly Brewer

Valiant, smart, great-hearted and beautiful old Toodle. I have had dreams about him, very ancient, but still alive and treasured like an old, old relic. He did live eighteen years and had long since greatly outgrown his name.

I named him Toodle when I brought him home from a friend, who had tired of a new litter of Siamese kittens and was eager to let him go cheaply. Toodle is an affectionate Southern expression for a small scraggly thing, and so he was. Had it been a few years later, and had I any intuition as to the animal he'd be, I probably would have called him Yoda.

I chose him, though he was tiny and wobbly, because he came to me more readily than the others and even then his azure blue eyes were special—extraordinarily large and almond-shaped. He had not been well cared for by either his mother or by my unconventional friend, a woman who felt that all babies, whether cat or human, should sooner rather than later be eating pureed greens. Her own baby and young children were unusually fussy, and the kitchen was always in a state of pandemonium with unwashed dishes and green splatters everywhere. Everything was noisy and chaotic. Even the purebred Siamese were scrawny, the kittens' mother apparently escaping away as often as she could, hardly bothering to feed or groom them.

I also chose this one because it occurred to me that he was the one who most needed to leave. I brought him home to our bright five-story walk-up apartment, filled with my own two young children and a troubled marriage. It wasn't the place or the time for a kitten, but I, who had always had cats, knew our airy apartment offered a nice home. So up the many steps we went–he in my arms as I had no cat carrier.

Immediately in the apartment, instead of sniffing around, he fled beneath a bed not to be lured out for hours. Finally, after he had rejected my many entreaties, I turned to preparing dinner for my children and for my husband, who might or might not arrive home. The scent of cooking was fragrant and soothing; we would have a nice dinner. Perhaps the aroma of a broiled roast coaxed him out from under the bed, for I could see the kitten had edged closer, but was still out of reach. Finally, I resorted to a gentle broom push and out he came, very trembly. I scooped him into my palm, ready to hold him close. Immediately there was a little

Avigdar Adams

sigh; and to the surprise of us both, a warm gush in my hand. Liquid spread through my fingers. His beautiful blue eyes looked at me in alarm, and he said in a small meow, as clearly as if he had spoken, "I'm sorry, couldn't hold it, and I am very hungry. The smell is so good. I want very much to eat." After rinsing my hand, I quickly gave him a thin slice of roast. That was our start of a long, loving mutual companionship during some of my most stressful years, which included several moves, all of which he took with aplomb.

Many times I was soothed by Toodle's presence, having him jump into my lap as though he knew I needed him, stroking his silky coat, looking deeply into his eyes and recognizing his knowing look of sympathy. All Siamese are talkers and he was certainly that. In fact, I learned enough minimal Siamese from him that we could converse a bit together. Quickly, he mastered an understanding of English vocabulary to the point where I could see in his eyes an effort to formulate a thought, a word. Then the look would fade and his eyes returned to the usual cat look, but his understanding of me and troubled situations never flagged. There were many difficult times, quarrels with my first husband, big moves with different adjustments to make–so many times when Toodle seemed to know how much I needed to hold him close, his concerned look telling me he understood I was unhappy.

Many years later, as a very old and infirm cat, he died making a last effort to greet me. I had had to work late and then pick up the children, who were with a neighbor, so he had evidently been waiting quite a while on the second floor, on my bed. He surely heard the car, the front door opening, my calling to him that I was home because as I came into the hallway, I saw him collapse halfway down the steps which he had reached, that being as far as the old bones could go. By the time I got to him, he was immobile, but looked at me in woozy recognition. I didn't move him, but covered him with a towel, propped his head up on a little pillow. He died peacefully in the night, but I knew that he knew the children and I were safe and there was no need to worry.

He led an adventurous life with several survivals. Once he was near disaster when he was most likely pushed over the old iron fire escape that wound up several stories of our apartment building. He used the fire escape frequently to gain access to the small back yard. As he was sure-footed, it is unlikely he misstepped on his own. In any case, the resulting wound to his leg was enormous. Somehow his grit and determination got him back up all the narrow stairs and onto the kitchen window. One leg was dangling, totally useless, but he had gotten himself up the many steps to home.

Treatment required a cast and being off his feet six weeks, which meant that I, as his nurse, had to assist him in eating and toileting, all of which he accepted with patience and understanding that to heal this is what had to happen. For the rest of his life he carried a limp, but it never seemed to bother him.

There was another occasion where he used his ingenuity and understanding in a situation that took him on a major journey. It is necessary to give a brief geography lesson first, so the effort of his undertaking can be understood. At the time, we had moved from the apartment to a house about a half block from Connecticut Avenue—an extremely busy thoroughfare full of buses, taxis and hurrying cars. Crossing was a challenge that required waiting for the stoplight down the street that never coincided with the traffic coming from the opposite direction, thus a hurried dash always had to be made to get across to where our street continued on, now into a pleasant residential neighborhood.

On the other side of Connecticut Avenue lived the Dudley family, our landlords. They were a pleasant older couple. I usually walked over to pay the rent and enjoyed the little evening visits. Sometimes I took Toodle, who liked to ride on my shoulder though visibly frightened by our Connecticut Avenue crossing. He would claw onto my shoulder, or scramble down my chest and burrow his head into my armpit as though he couldn't bear to watch.

Our street ended into an entry to Rock Creek Park–a large public park in the heart of Washington, D. C., full of large trees, dense undergrowth and hilly terrain. A few blocks south of our street, Connecticut Avenue rose to a high overpass and the park ran beneath it, but never in a straight line. Rather, it meandered in and out, up and down, eventually some edges running into the Dudley yard. There was no simple direct route to their house through the park. By this time in my life there were two other Siamese cats, my two children growing fast, and still my marriage that continued in an uneasy relationship. My husband and I planned a vacation. We had a house sitter and off we went without the children and with no concerns. Then we decided to prolong our trip with the sitter's agreement.

Upon our return home, the sitter declared, "I hate to tell you, but Toodle has gone missing; the children and the other cats are fine. I've called and called, but Toodle's been gone for days."

I cried out in alarm, "How unlike him! Did you put up notices?"

"No, I just called him."

I was devastated–my beloved Toodle gone, without a trace. Some days later, I walked to the Dudleys to pay the rent, missing terribly my companion on my shoulder. As I came up their front steps, I heard a rush in the bushes and suddenly there was Toodle on my shoulder–breathless, full of his own relief and excitement.

Mr. Dudley watched the reunion in amazement. "Is that your animal you usually bring? Well for goodness sake. It never occurred to me, though we've been feeding him ... found him in the back yard, you know where the park edges. He was all dirty and full of scratches, pretty forlorn and very thirsty. He's been hanging around for days. Come to think of it, it's like he's been waiting. Never occurred to me that he was yours. He's obviously come up from the park through a rough journey."

I looked at Toodle, who seemed to understand. I felt him say, "Yes, you were gone and a good long time it was. I didn't trust the sitter, so I went to find you, thinking you'd turn up at the Dudleys'. I couldn't cross the Avenue even for you, so I went through the park. I had no idea how it turns and wanders, how rough it is. I didn't want to go back to that bad, unfriendly sitter. Now, just like I thought, here you are."

Oh Toodle, what mixed-up human, but presumably logical cat thinking! Home we went, he riding comfortably on my shoulder.

# Wedding Cat

by Richard Stone

A yellow flash, golden at the core
Joins us heart to heart;
My stiff and frozen sinews have been thawed a little.
Watching cat's adult tread—the ripple of flank, the plume of tail
Flexible and poised as a tightrope walker—
I reminisce on his kittenhood:
The freckled nose, the echoing pink of paws and mouth. Quiet furry breaths.
Then startled wakening,
Scrutinizing eyes, an unfurled leap
And a drunkard's exit.

If such thoughts,
Past doting on the in-striped spiral beauty of his rest,
Beg explanation, then recall
That from the first
He was the marriage of blue eyes and red-gold hair.
You had the know-how, I the patience
I attentiveness, you flair:
Together we raised a fine, sturdy, loving soul.
You left me, and him to me, because
Leaving was the most important.

Avigdar Adams

But you laugh at his ways, and wince at his fight-torn flesh

As if your spirit yet comprehends his in some fashion.

He is the marriage of blue eyes and gold-red hair.

I watch over him, nourish and shelter him,

And hope that with time

The gaping wound in his side will heal.

Perhaps it's superstition

Still I know that I will love you while he stays with me.

As precious as is love is orange cat.

# Not Tidbits But ... Catnip

by Richard Stone

Listen to people talking to cats. You'll find we typically repeat ourselves as in, "Does Lulu want some tuna … does Lulu want some tuna?" I postulate this reason: it's because they don't answer.

I once had a cat named Mitzi, a beautiful muted calico who was hateful to everyone but me. So naturally, I loved her. I used to call her M. Puss, and that led to a game where I would use that name in terrible puns, such as:

Q. What does Mitzi do when she sleeps? A. She dreams the M-pussible dream.

Q. Who is Mitzi's favorite royal personage? A. The M-puss of Japan

Q. What do they say about Mitzi's senile grandfather? A. He's non-m-puss-mentis

As William Blake wrote, "Enough. Or too much."

The last place I lived while Mitzi was with me was a rental that went up for sale. That was impetus to plan an extended overseas sojourn. But what to do with Mitzi? No worry. A month before I left I discovered that she had found herself a welcoming home down the street where she'd be well taken care of. I was relieved.

At that same house, four of us shared space and rent. As it happened, we each had a cat, and they generally got on. One housemate left and a cat-less fellow moved in. About that time a loud-mouthed aggressive Siamese started nosing around. Three of us wanted to chase her away, but the new guy insisted on adopting her. How did she know she'd find a hero? And soon afterwards, it became evident that she was pregnant. After adopting two out, we were left with two more mouths to feed. New-housemate and I became a couple (and still are some thirty-five years later). The cats were cared for by one of the remaining housemates, though in new quarters, while we did our traveling; and when we got back, the Siamese Mama was the one cat we wound up with. She became a very sweet and loving friend.

At an advanced age, Mama died. The next day my partner heard a sound under his car in the driveway. On checking, he found a baby Siamese, a virtual replica of Mama, awaiting his discovery. Enter Putter-tat, stage left.

Catnip all gone.

# Only One Ramsay

by Polly Brewer

Even as a kitten he was an opinionated animal with very strong likes and dislikes, and he never hid his feelings. Once, I was petting him and for surely reasons of his own, he did the most unexpected act of leaping up and biting my lip. I cried out in surprise and pain, horrified at what he had done. He raced out into a cold wet day, stayed out for hours in an icy drizzle, then came in and came over to me as if uncertain what to say. He didn't know what had happened but was sorry; I could tell that. It never occurred again. He was not vicious, yet something had set him off that one time. All his long life, he was like no other cat. He was ever Ramsay, a law unto himself. Here is a diary entry.

Now that he's old, Ramsay has been given another chance. He made it clear that's what he wants and is aware, I think, that he's got it. He may even be grateful.

For some months, he had an open sore on his upper front leg that did not heal, nor infect, either. No hair grew over the sore, and it began to look like a salami slice pasted on his skin. Never one to pay much attention to personal grooming, now he began to lick it constantly.

Ramsay seemed in no pain, no limping, no languor, good appetite. Of course, we took him to the veterinarian as the sore persisted and enlarged. The vet said what we feared—a spreading skin cancer. My first feeling was, "So be it." Sad, yes, but he'd had a long healthy, happy life. We'll wait until his appetite and spirits flag and let him go easily. The vet disagreed. He didn't think the cancer had reached the bone, and there was still good chance the cleaned area had enough skin to be stitched back together. We said we'd wait a little longer and see.

Ramsay continued on for a bit, but then began to attack the salami patch—gnawing at it viciously. So in spite of the cost, and with sighs from my second husband, Don, and myself, the old cat goes back to the vet for surgery.

Polly Brewer

Just like a human before an operation, he goes off early with no breakfast in him. He is highly noisy about that, but once in the car he begins to tremble, apparently knowing perfectly well that the trip is to the vet again. I swear he seems to know every turn and stop light—each one bringing him closer and closer. His breath makes a strange "uhuh" sound, somewhere between a nervous purr and an unnervingly human sob.

Our vet says to call in an hour or so and expects all to go well. He is cheerful as he tells us we can probably pick him up late afternoon as he will recuperate faster at home, as long as he is kept quiet.

Then the wait—the news is good. Vet thinks he got it all, says if the cancer had reached the lymph nodes, there is serious trouble ahead, but, as of now, all is well. I expected a huge bandage or a bulky cat collar, but there is just an ingenious array of stitches devised of staples and gut, with a bitter apple scent sprayed over the area as a further deterrent against biting. "He's still woozy but do keep him quiet and, if we are lucky, he'll keep his mouth away from the thicket I've devised." He had done his part well. The line of stitches was long and he had been careful to make wide margins.

Ramsay knows he is going home, for there is no more trembling or raspy breathing. His eyes are glazed, but he notes each turn, raising his head languidly at each of them.

Soon home, I put him in his favorite sleeping spot, pet him gently and hope he will settle down. Hopeless thought. He does not look dazed any more. In no time, he struggles up from his bed and totters drunkenly to the kitchen. When he is hungry or out of sorts, he makes a loud "araugh" sound, then "wearhroo, wearhroo" repeatedly. I give him a little food. It is soon gone. He "araughes" for more. He eats the equivalent of the unoffered breakfast and a hearty early dinner. I think it's a long way from a human coming out of anesthesia; if Ramsay's queasy, there's no hint.

Then he makes his softer "earoo" sound that I have often thought is his baby voice he uses when he sees us eating ice cream and is asking nicely for some. I give him a spoonful, which he eagerly laps up. Then he drinks prodigiously of fresh water and goes to the cat door, which has been blocked with a chair that he, with determination, attempts to push aside with his stitched paw. He looks at me, his eyes now wide open and furious—"araugh, araugh," he says with force. So I, sighing, let him out, knowing that keeping him quiet is not possible.

He goes, wobbling, but determined, to his favorite toilet place in the leaves behind the swimming pool deck. He sniffs carefully at several places, almost falling down, until he finds the place he wants, settles himself for a truly voluminous elimination. He shuts his eyes, stretches his mouth in a cat smile in what is obviously exquisite relief. We exchange a congratulatory look. Both he and I know he's been a good fellow to have held it so long.

Over the years, he and I have had many walks together in the garden, especially when I am showing it to someone, but when it is just myself, he often loses interest altogether. Frequently, he takes his own walk on the inner edge of our irregularly paved flagstone swimming pool. To my amazement, it is this rim that he now heads for, maybe giving himself two inches instead of one. I say sternly, "No, Ramsay, you cannot do that." He clearly hears my alarm. In response, he flicks his ears, moves his Manx stump of a tail (in cat show parlance, he is a stumpy, not a rumpy, meaning he has a vestige of a tail as against no tail at all). Neither of us makes any further move or sound. We both know a standoff when we see it. Then he shakes himself, begins to totter along, his high back legs not near as wobbly as they were a few minutes ago.

I am thinking I'll have to make a fast greatly unwanted jump into a very cold pool to haul him out, and I know I can't do that. I have a fear of diving though I am a good swimmer, and the water in early springtime is frigid. In my mind, I see him falling to the bottom like a ripe plum, too surprised to make a struggle. I think how upset the vet would be even if I rescued Ramsay in time to prevent drowning, for the wound would surely be severely damaged. I lean down to grab him, no more warning or scolding. His growl and his total look of fierceness and determination stop me again. In a long life with cats, I've never heard one growl. From Ramsay, it is a vicious sound. I am looking at primeval survival of the fittest, a personal quest at its very heart. I see this instinct in full force. Those huge black pupils tell me clearly, "I can, will walk this pool edge, it is something I have to do, so let me alone." He hisses and snarls at me. I back away. He finishes the whole circumference of the pool's edge unsteadily but carefully.

Then he turns to the garden. A friendly look says, "Now, you may follow." I do. It takes some minutes as he stops frequently to sniff many areas. I wonder how long he thinks he's been away in cat years, hours, days? He finally finishes his inspection and leads the way to his cat door. He waits for me to open it for him, then makes his sweet noise "erhroo," which seems to mean, "Here I am, thanks for letting me in." He stalks in, still stiff, but no more wobble, and goes behind the sofa, to a hard-to-reach spot. He stretches out with a grunt, sleeps for several hours. Don feels the need to check on him several times to make sure he is still breathing. I have no doubt.

The deterrent on his wound works well. Ramsay never touches his leg. Two weeks later we are back at the vet for stitch removal. No trembling in the car! Though I hold him tightly, he patiently allows the stitches to be clipped away. There is some trust going on. From his ill temper at being brushed and his scene at the swimming pool edge, I had expected a major biting attempt. Did he somehow associate the doctor with feeling better? The leg looks fine, no swelling or pain. Doctor says we can now only wait and see if he holds lucky. Chemo and radiation are not an avenue that Ramsay and I will walk together.

Here we come home, Ramsay presses against me to better look out the window. Everything about him is alert and in good humor, with no more angst or anxieties. He walks outside, sticking his leg out to catch the sun. With sleepy eyes, half open and a clear yellow, he watches me idly as I move about in the garden. He has no more need for a full inspection. He acts for all the world like a nice old gentleman just enjoying his familiar bright lazy morning.

Polly Brewer

# Gordon's Domain

## by Polly Brewer

I heard someone ask Polly the other day why the cat let so many squirrels and birds live in the yard. She said something like "Gordie doesn't seem interested." True enough—I've never been much of a hunter. I like to catch small things and I can be very fast, though I admit it is for sport, you know, not really any territory thing.

Anyway, I thought her brief comments were nowhere as complete or complimentary as they should have been. Besides, I understand perfectly well that it is my yard now and territory just comes with it. So, if you want to listen, I'll give you an answer, but sure, I'll admit all those birds and squirrels are a pain—they are insistently loud with all their rrrrrchitchits and squark-skars. Honestly, though, it's a big yard and I can always go under the shade of the bushes or onto the screen porch, put my paws over my ears and forget about them. I do wish the jays weren't quite so noisy and mean. They even come at me if I am walking away pretending I'm not even bothered.

Back to this territory thing, as I have given it quite a lot of thought. It's a frame of mind, you see, and I have reluctantly had to learn about it. It's been a long time now, but when I came here I was already half grown and had been on my own for some time. Scary! I was never what you'd call a street cat; somehow I hadn't been born to it. I knew about warmth and someone to pet me, so I must have been born in a nice place. All of those things are still important to me. In truth, I think territories are not necessities.

I'll also add that I have always been very light-toned, and it was not easy to hide anywhere safely. My undersides and legs are white with a pale orange jacket over my back. My shoulders are white with a few spots of orange and more orange covers my head like a small cap. My tail is long and full with neat rings of pale orange circling white. People exclaim when they see me, "What a pretty boy." That is something Polly says frequently, too, so I suppose I am pleasing to look at. I do know that I am very particular about keeping clean; it upsets me to be dirty. I am most willing to spend time every day cleaning myself everywhere, even between my toes. It is a luxurious feeling to sit in a sunny patch picking out stickers, feeling my tongue all over my body. If it is hot, I can roll over on my back and stretch out my legs to sleep, the white fur all exposed, somewhat like I am dressed in white pajamas she tells me.

Well, years ago, while I was on the street, it began to get cold, so I understood that I had to do something because being cold is the most dismal feeling possible. I had met Polly earlier. I had been sleeping rough and I had gotten a horrible stinking wad of gasoline and pine tar pitch in the middle of my back. I could not get at it no matter how I twisted and snapped. She had spoken to me nicely, said she saw the trouble and would I let her pick me up and take me into her house where she would help me. I was relieved. I held still and tried to be patient as she clipped off some especially sticky stuff and then dabbed at my back with water.

Soon I could feel my back was clean again. I would have stayed with her right then, but there was another big cat around, very heavy and fluffy, who hissed at me meanly; so that time I left reluctantly and returned to the street. It's curious, now that I think about it, how I got on that street. I was by myself on another, not as nice, when a young girl picked me up and brought me to this one. Her family did not want me, I guess, because they gave me nothing to eat and kept telling me to go away. They would truly shut the door in my face. It was a nice street, quiet with lots of trees and well-kept front yards, not mean at all, yet there was no place for me there. Polly noticed me and even offered some welcome food; this was before my back had such a mess on it. Some weeks passed and the nights were becoming quite cold. I had just spent an awful one where I couldn't get warm at all before the damp early morning arrived. I felt truly miserable, so I figured if I climbed over a fence, it would put me in the back where she lived. I had seen the big cat do it several times, so I had a good idea that there must be a way to get into the house. It was easy to pick up the cat's scent. It led onto a back porch and into a little opening in the wall. How strange! He had his own door. I had never seen such a thing. Following his scent and gathering up my nerve, I went on in through his door. I was inside a dark cupboard of some sort, but I could smell exactly what the big cat had done. He had butted his head against another little door. Before I lost my nerve, I did the same thing. In a second, I popped into the kitchen where she had taken me before. There she was—both she and the big cat staring at me in amazement. To this day I don't know why he didn't dive at me. I needed to tell him quickly that I hadn't come as an intruder. I had learned that much street sense. I gathered my wits and lay down before him, paws up. It was a promise gladly given and, yes, carefully observed that I wasn't after his land, or his house, or her; I just wanted to be there with them.

The old cat made no jump, so I got up and looked around. Excited now, I began to move my feet up and down on the floor, like I was kneading. They just kept looking at me; no one made a move. Somehow, we all understood that I had come to stay. The old cat had no tail, just a funny stump surrounded by fluff. He moved it at me slowly. I stared. I'd never seen such a thing. Soon, Polly was giving me food in a place quite separate from the big cat, who answered to "Ramsay." She continued to feed us separately. I believe Ramsay appreciated the peace and quiet of not sharing a food dish as much as I did. Still, that never kept him from checking my leftovers. I've never had a big appetite, so there were often leftovers that he always seemed to enjoy.

I kept my bargain with him, and by doing that, it was bliss right from the start. I also found there were two laps to welcome me, for Polly has an extremely nice mate, whom I also came to love dearly. Amazingly, Ramsay didn't care about laps at all. He liked to lie on feet or empty shoes. He seemed to dislike being picked up, so I have both laps to myself. I also enjoy a warm quilt and a sweater or a cushion to lie upon. They, too, were provided. Ramsay preferred his own basket. I must tell you, though, that neither Ramsay nor I ever tried to take over each other's favorite spot. I never even went near to sniff his basket, so now you are beginning to see why territory has never been on my priority list.

Another thing about Ramsay was he had almost no tail. I would often check his rear, trying to figure it out, but there really was almost nothing there except a big fluff. He hated me to do that and would try to catch me by turning around quickly with a curse and a swat. After a while, when he would walk by without even a wave of a fluff greeting, I would lean over to touch him as he passed. Then he would always yell, like he had been hurt. Always then, Polly would pet us both, saying "Boys, boys, no fighting." It always seemed to gripe Ramsay that I almost never said a word. He was meowing all the time, full of conversation, but I have always found it difficult to speak. With the humans, I can always look at them and wave my tail. They never seemed bothered by my lack of a voice, but boy, it sure did irritate Ramsay.

Yet whenever our people were away, we never fought at all. Often, we slept in the same room, he in his basket and me on a chair. We'd listen for the car crunch on the gravel and the key in the door. Then we would both get up and go to the door together—no punches from either of us.

There was no question, though, that Ramsay was the lord of the land. He patrolled the whole back area regularly, even when it was cold or rainy. He kept all other cats away, and I admired him for that and was grateful. I could go out in the yard at any hour and there was absolutely no other animal to be afraid of. Yes, there weren't as many noisy squirrels and birds around either. The peace was lovely. Why he was willing to let me use his door and tolerate my scent remains a mystery. Certainly, he never tolerated any other animal.

Well, some years ago, he began to slow down. Once, I remember it very well, a big orange cat came into the front yard. Ramsay made no move to run out and chase him away, but jumped up on the window sill and began to curse him, his lips drawn back in an ugly way. I looked at him in amazement. Why hadn't he run out? Then he looked at me and started to curse me too. I understood him to say, "So go on! Get him, you fool. Run on and run him off. Go! Go! Go!"

I did the best I could, not accustomed to chasing other cats, yet I am fast and agile. The orange stranger was startled and dashed away. I came back in and looked proudly at Ramsay. He was still at the window and had watched everything closely. After that, he no longer chased intruders. He would curse at me to do it. Now, too, when he went out on his nightly patrol, he would grunt at me to follow him, and I did. It was kind of like I was covering his back. I guess that was my training about territory, but still, it did not seem a big deal—in fact, more like a royal pain. I was just following Ramsay, but I began to know what he did and where we went.

Increasingly, Ramsay began to lie around in his basket and when he did get up, he did not seem too steady. One day they took him off and when they came back, Ramsay was still in the basket, but it wasn't him at all. His smell was different. I checked the place where he ate, but there was no dish there. Even the newspaper had been taken up. Polly was very sad. I watched as they dug a hole and laid a stiff non-Ramsay in it, now wrapped in a blanket.

I knew that the land I had never wanted or cared much for was now mine to guard. I understood I had to do what he did—check it all the time, chase others off. I'm doing the best I can, but it is hard and boring work. Some areas I've cut back on a lot. After several vicious tangles with a tough gray that Polly calls the marauder, I have found it better to race away rather than confront him. I feel ashamed about this, but several times now, he has really pinned me to the ground. He has a way of jumping on me suddenly with no warning, biting my neck which brings out blood and scratching at my eyes. He means business, and I have learned to fear and avoid him the best I can.

It's a huge relief to jump through my door and find safe haven in the kitchen, but I am down in spirit, being bloody and covered with the attacker's slobber. Polly does what she can to help me clean up, but I just want to be left alone; I feel terrible. It usually takes a full day or so to feel like myself. She tells me, too, that the marauder is an extra mean cat, and it's a good thing to run when I see him, but I do feel sad about it. That gray cat is the only unpleasant thing in my otherwise perfect life. It is truly terrifying to be on the ground, wondering wildly how I can only get the strength to throw him off and, in the same instant, jump up and run for my door. Fighting back isn't even in question.

I'll end this by telling you one more thing about territory. There are other cats in the yard next to ours. My family and theirs are friendly. I hear them talking to each other frequently; there are a lot of "be nice" cat talks on both sides. There is an old big furry female and a very pretty young black one. I like them both well enough and have not chased the black one off when she comes into our yard. I know she will soon leave as she is just sniffing around and the old one is like Ramsay—no longer able to do much but lie in the sun in her own yard. Food is often kept outside for them on a screen porch that also has a cat door. I think it is great fun to eat out, and every now and then I go in their door and help myself. The cat girls never mind. Well, one day there was a young black and white. We were introduced carefully. "Good little Lenny" and "Nice boy Gordie," you know, that kind of stuff. I knew everyone wanted me and Lenny to hit it off. I thought I'd give it a try. We sniffed each other; I was careful not to hiss.

Well, before I knew it, Lenny had grown into a big cat and was coming over my fence all the time and even sleeping in one of my favorite spots. My yard is more interesting than his, for I have many more shady spots and spaces to lounge, but still it didn't seem right for him to barge over all the time. He just wants to hang out, not fight, but now Lenny runs off when he sees me like he's actually afraid of me. Some good he'd be as a friend or a tag-along patroller! I realize that he just likes to hang out in my yard, but still, it doesn't set too well with me. It is, after all, my own sunlit yard, I admit it, my territory.

It is an agreeable feeling that this place is all mine: sunshine, loving laps, warm bed, food when I like. My only wish is never to see the marauder again, for he may jump me without warning, and I will be frightened and bitten and perhaps need another trip to the vet. And yes, I miss Ramsay so very much.

Avigdar Adams

Timothy Savage

# Cat Eyes

by Julie Harcos

Curious, cautious, contemptuous . . . enigmatic, evasive, eerie feral cats! The first awareness of strange cats in the yard is their eyes, looking across space, through glass, waiting, sneaking, step-by-tentative step, eye contact and they turn tail and disappear.

There are three categories of feral cat: the curious, the cautious and the contemptuous. The curious ones don't run off so fast. They may even once have known owners, as an over-supply of kittens often results in sneaky drop-offs in the foothills and mountains. Sink or swim! This usually spells death from coyote, bobcat, bear or mountain lion. If they survive they learn to be wary but retain latent memories of human kindness. These cats are owed a chance for survival. When caught, they are taken to an area where feral cats are appreciated–no other cats, lots of ground squirrels, gophers and water.

The cautious cats are probably offspring of "barn cats," feral survivors, fed and appreci-ated by sympathetic humans in need of rodent control in outbuildings. Cats wanted! No affec-tion necessary. Must hunt. Aggression discouraged. Food supplemented as needed. Shelter available. These cats refuse human contact, hide their babies, teach them survival skills and chase them away as they get older. These juvenile cats know to be cautious and learn to be aggressive. They become marauders that steal food and mark the territory belonging to their docile, spoiled, totally domestic and pampered cousins, uppity cats of mountain residents.

The resident wussy pussies rely on their humans to eliminate the competition. This class of feral cat has a special destination. Since they can be nasty, they hiss, growl, and fight; they need to go where their skills match the human terrain. Their personality and mode of survival gets them released in the vicinity of the Nazi Pig farmer in the foothills east of Fresno. Fish or cut bait along with the pigs and the peacocks!

The contemptuous cats are the worst of the lot. They are enigmatic, evasive and eerie; they display an elemental enmity. To the extent that humans anthropomorphize animals, one could attribute malevolent tendencies to this cat. It is a mystery where he comes from. He has the look of a bobcat mix. It is this cat that comes to the yard, eyes hooded, stance aggressive, ready to fight or flee. If he encounters cats he fights and bites. If he makes eye contact he is gone in a flash, but not too far. He owns wherever he invades. He's mean. His eyes convey a message—beware! Capture is imperative. Easy to say! He knows traps and is exceptional at evading capture. Bait the trap, sit back and wait. Wet food, dry food, he senses the danger and remains at large.

It becomes guerilla warfare. This cat is determined to chase off or kill the rightful cats. One cat is bitten and develops an abscess. One doesn't come home for days, then comes back limping with a bite infection. The trap meanwhile has managed to lure an unsuspecting raccoon, and each of the family cats has spent a night behind bars. Food can no longer be left out. The family cats are nervous, anxious, jumpy. The peace that existed in the haven of the yard evaporates and fear is palpable. Any attempt at a weapon is futile. He seems to be able to read minds. Step into his line of sight, he knows the instant he is spotted and is gone in a blink. His instinct is honed to survival at all cost.

In the end, capture turns out to be quite simple. Disguise the trap. Drape it with a blanket. Make it into a cave. A little dry food under the mesh, the cat has to enter to eat. With this trick of camouflage (Who would have thought it necessary?) feral cats are caught invariably on the first night. Where can a distinctly antisocial cat be placed? There is no room in the mountains for a cat like this. It survives at the expense of other cats. Not wild enough to stay in the wild. Too wild to be part of a domestic milieu. A sad and dangerous misfit; release feels inappropriate.

Though perhaps not the answer for all feral cats, as most deserve a chance at life, this one courted death. A humane death. A trip to the city and a final stop at the animal shelter, the place equipped and authorized to mark the end. Farewell to a menace, but oh, the memory of those eyes.

# The Bruiser

by Polly Brewer and Kathy Wosika

This cat tale, told to me by Kathy Wosika, fine ceramicist, paper maker and teacher, was irresistible to write about. About a year or so ago, a feral cat was a frequent visitor in Kathy's lush garden. In no way ingratiating or mild, the cat was a big, square-jawed, strong-shouldered gray-striped tom. He had only a fierce scowl of arrogance whenever he was spoken to–never a hint of "I'll be your friend, if you like."

He was equally ill-willed toward Kathy's two aging cats, Max and Roshi, and he would try to start a fight on any pretext. In fact, he was a bully of an animal, hugely self-sufficient and tough. They called him "The Bruiser."

One fall weekend, Kathy and her husband were to be away at two different meetings. Kathy left first, making sure that the familiar cat feeder was full and in its usual place. Their two family cats lived outdoors and were used to the freedom of their yard, which afforded many hiding places from the sour attacker.

Later, her husband, who may have been working outside in the garden, realized the lateness of the hour and dashed into his car (already packed for the trip) and drove away. For whatever reason, the front door of the house was left ajar.

Two days later Kathy arrived home first, to be met by the open front door. Her heart in her throat, she feared the worst–rooms and possessions emptied or, worse still, maybe a robbery currently in progress. For a moment, she thought she would call the police, but there was no sign of an unknown car on the street. Not a fearful person, she entered her home, anxiously expecting the worst.

Amazed and overwhelmed with relief, she quickly saw that nothing had been disturbed. As she entered the living room, her eyes fell upon the large red sofa. To her surprise, curled up and sleeping in comfort and warmth, was the Bruiser. Kathy's unexpected appearance awakened him. He looked right up at her. Instantly he sprang from the couch and blazed out the front door before either could realize what had just happened. Kathy ran out to the porch and saw him staring back from the driveway as if to say, "The use of your nice pad suited me and now you've ruined it."

Next, she found Max and Roshi cuddled together on the soft couch in the music room, enjoying such pleasures as had never been offered them before because of their outdoor-living status. When they saw Kathy at the door both cats chose to test the situation. With a yawn and a stretch, they stayed put and waited for what would come next. It was such a sweet and tender sight that Kathy gave them a pass for the afternoon.

The Bruiser continued to roam through the yard. Often he would lie down in the shade of a bush or shrub to escape the heat of summer; however, he never attempted to test his luck with an open front door again.

John Barnard

# Our Israeli Cat

by Richard Stone

How changed Ruth is.
The few weeks without a home have been hard on her.
Her coat, so fine to the fingers, has coarsened.
Her peaked head surmounts a tube of a neck, and she is balding behind the ears.
Twice we have stuffed her in a knapsack, carried her some miles and
left her to make a new life while
we traveled on—
only, on returning, to find her, scruffy and forlorn, also to have returned.
To what? What value is such instinct?
YOUR HOUSEHOLD IS REMOVED
YOUR LICENSE TO WELL-BEING REVOKED!

Her young ones were snatched away early—
opportunity arose and it's no easy matter to find homes these days for poor dependent beasts.
Milk still engorged her teats so the veins showed.
For two days she prowled and growled around
calling her children
turning on her side as if to feed them.
Then there were again just us
to bring her table scraps and leban,
offer the soft blue blanket for her nap.
A simple black-and-white patchwork cat
grown beautiful
in care and familiarity.
Even her 3:00 a.m. navigations across our beds
became precious

as if the irritant produced a pearl:
this is Ruthy, our Israeli cat.
It is time to leave again, this time for good,
and Ruthy must be dispatched to make her way alone.
First her kits gone
now us and her home.
For us she won't even know to grieve.
We abandon her to history.
Some said, "You're leaving in a few months,
how can you take her in?
When you leave, what then?"
They might have been right.
But without her our stay would not have seemed
so dear
so clear of import:
it is us she summons shrilly to the door
and us she trails
dropping stealthily from a branch.
Always to remember "Take the lunch bag for Ruth, is there
milk for the puss?"
is always to know
that time has passed, that time demands anew.
And even yet the soft purr rises with her breathing flanks
of terrestrial black 'midst seas of white.
It is not easy to find a place these days
and occasion calls us elsewhere.
But oh you cat of Israel
we'll not forget

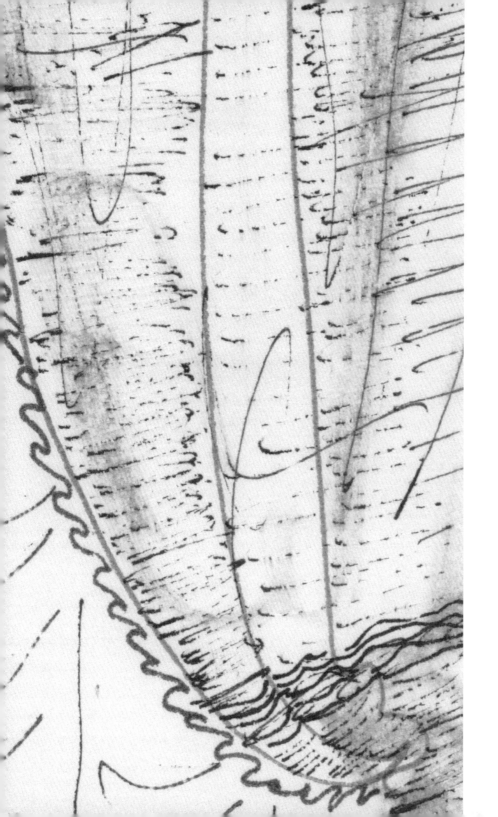

# Cats of Fancy

Selections from

# Miss Emmaline La Chatte's Complete Book Of Feline Beauty & Purr-Fect Etiquette

by Richard Stone

Illustrations by Benjamin Locke

# *Part 1: For The Men*

**ATTIRE**
Gentlemen cats
Should only wear spats
When casually browsing
Outdoors, or when mousing.

A derby is sporting
When Sir Puss goes a-courting
But for formal occasions
A topper
Is proper.

**CAUDAL CONDUCT**
A gentlecat's tail is not to chase
Not to be used in a circle race
It's there to be plumed
As if perfumed
Betokening poise and grace.

A gentlecat's tail is not a flail
For swatting flies or setting sail
It's nonchalance, legato,
Never staccato.

When at rest on a stoop
One's tail should drape, not droop.

# *Part 2: For The Ladies*

ON THE FEMININE FELINE'S
AFTERNOON BEAUTY REST
ON THE DINING TABLE
A placemat
Is just right for a lady cat,
But in a pinch or two
A napkin will do.

IN DEFENSE OF A LADY'S VIRTUE
Sharpened claws
In delicate paws
Breed respect
Not kittens.
Discourteous beaux
Need sabre toes
Not handling with
Kid mittens.

WINDOW SILL CONDUCT
The sill is reserved
For being observed
For making one's morning debut.
Finish toilette
Before getting set
Into the public view.
When on display
Remember the way
You behave is a public disclosure.

*Cat Tales*

No licking of paws
Or opening jaws
Don't move save
with gravest composure.

A nice flower pot
For curling about
Can add to one's elegance.
But whatever your grace
With a fine china vase
You're taking a bit of a chance.

A casual stare
At the whole thoroughfare
And at all passersby will suffice.
Lower eyes just a touch
Twitch your tail if you must
But no rising–not even for mice.

On the sill, for Emmaline's sake,
Be still, reputation's at stake.

# *Part 3: For all my disciples*

FINAL WORDS
It's time, dear friends, to bid adieu
And say, "Henceforth it's up to you
To be a mean and petty cat
Or follow purr-fect etti-cat."
Well-mannered cats find open doors
Are welcomed in with open paws
To homes of highest rank and station
To royal fete and celebration.
The key to any noble house
Is the minding of one's purrs and mr-eows.
So take your choice, chase alley mice,
Or follow Emmaline's advice.

If you don't, when falling low,
Remember that I told you so.

But yours a life that's warm and fine
For paying heed to Emmaline.

Avigdar Adams

# Portals

by Richard Stone

She wasn't sure she hadn't imagined it–a faint whisper of a mew. There. Again. She laughed at how imperative such a faint sound could be. While putting down her work and going out to look.

It was there, of course; and now recognized, it became all voice, so the tiny charcoal gray body could hardly be seen behind the aura of sound. It became what she called a porch cat. She named it—Miss Mouth—fed it and, by the third day, could pet it. A porch cat, unlike a house cat, had no indoor privileges and no health insurance. Otherwise, it was as good as a pet.

By the next Thursday, a big yellow tom had begun hanging around the side of the house, waiting for leftovers.

By Sunday a Siamese mix with squinty eyes was also lurking.

By the next week she had identified three others, and one was pregnant.

Steve Norton

# Triumph

## Written & Illustrated by J.H. Livingston

It was the third time that week Chairman Meow got his head stuck in the mini blinds. He was not amused. Once someone finally came in the room (he had to yowl for quite a while before anyone took notice) he stood there and laughed for an achingly long time. Then, without … freeing him from entrapment in the tricky blind, the onlooker left. Humans. Meanwhile, old Hissyfit was happily eating her fancy food and living the high life. The only acknowledgement of Meow's situation she conceded was an irritated backward twitch of an ear. The Chairman yowled louder, raising his voice to a level only achieved by the most accomplished Siamese yowlers. Though the talent ran deep in his lineage, it had taken years of dedication to the craft to reach such sonority, such hair-raising decibel levels, such dizzying pitch. For a moment he lost himself in his own grandeur, captivated by his artistry. The physical predicament of the blinds was forgotten amidst the poetic wail of tragedy.

Meow's reverie ended abruptly with the sound of a mechanical snap. The human who'd so heartlessly abandoned him moments earlier had returned, now accompanied by the Small One. In keeping with his lack of camaraderie, the taller human offered no assistance. Instead, he dashed about the room pointing a small box at The Chairman who remained pinned between the blinds, all dignity having melted away. It was almost as bad as being in the bath—almost. The Small One stood laughing. Neither attempted to come to his aid. Meow resumed his wailing, this time accompanied by a frantic pawing at the blinds. Did the humans not understand? He was trapped! The Tall One was talking, little of it making any sense. He came up to Meow, pointed the box inches from his face and issued a succession of loud clicks. Meow hissed, making it clear what he thought of the human and its clicking box.

The Tall One went on babbling, "Oh that was a good one! What a shot! Hold on; I'll get you out of there, Chairman Meow. No need to hiss…" It seemed to The Chairman that there certainly had been the need. The Tall One continued, "Let's see, you really got yourself tangled in here, gosh your head is big." Coming from something with such a disproportionately large head, this seemed a rather stupid thing to say, thought Chairman Meow, but then, most of what humans said was rather stupid.

Immediately upon feeling the clench of the blinds release his neck, The Chairman

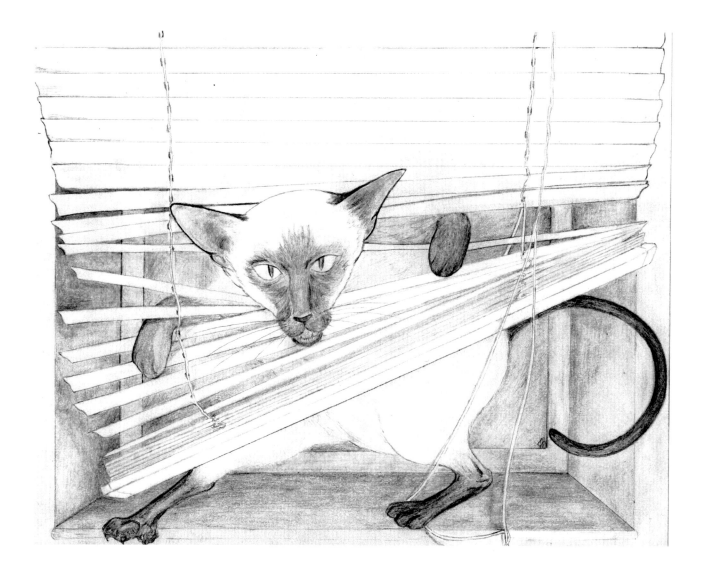

jumped from the sill and made a dash for sanctuary. He was intercepted mid-stride by The Small One—swung up into the air and flipped upside-down. Meow came to a halt staring up into big round eyes and a gaping mouth. He struggled to right himself but she was too strong for him. She held fast, cooed, chattered and jiggled him about. Unfazed by his attempt to escape, Meow's captor carried him down the hall with a bouncing stride.

Round the corner, into the Small One's lair, he was dumped onto a soft pile. She had not yet tidied her area and the heap of fabric was rumpled and warm. Clearly it had recently been transported from the hot danger-chamber. Though he'd heard the cat legends of the horrors of that machine, he'd come to appreciate its ability to cozy a pile of clothing. Meow avoided the machine, but kept an eye on the comings and goings of the laundry so he might take advantage of its powers.

The Small One understood this and in spite of the Tall One's disapproval, she often snuck The Chairman into her lair to bask in the warmth and sweet scents. For a blissful time, before piece by piece it was pulled out from under him, folded and shut into cabinets, Chairman Meow was king of a small mountain of good feeling. Forgetting his anger at being snatched, Meow settled in to the pile while the Small One snuggled in too, and they both fell asleep.

Dreaming, Chairman Meow traversed a vast country. His senses keen, the world around him spoke of many things. A slight breeze danced by his face, sending vibrations along each hair that told him something of where the wind came from. Tilting his nose up to catch a passing scent, he gathered news of the far countryside. The earth and all living things spoke to him here—their resonance felt in every sensation.

Jostled to wakefulness, Meow found himself atop a diminishing mound. Ignoring this unpleasant reality, he closed his eyes. Another upset and he was rolled over the edge of his mountain, any chance of sleep whisked away along with the shirt he'd been lying on.

Still not quite in the land of the humans, Meow sat up and stretched. He felt uncomfortably flat on one side of his body. Never one to allow such asymmetry, he shook himself, gave a few quick scratches and began grooming the offending fur. The methodical process channeled his attention back to the waking world. By the time his coat was orderly and slick, The Chairman was alert and completely present. The dream lands, banished for a time, gave way to the realm of the house and its known routine.

A low, coarse rattling came from the other room. Meow perked up instantly. It sounded again, this time accompanied by the food song. He thought it strange that Humans sang whenever they fed him. They seemed to enjoy it. It wasn't the emotional poetry of mystery and longing that his kind had worked into an art, but it had a certain appeal. He jumped down from the bed and trotted into the kitchen. Once there, he greeted the Tall One with a meow of acknowledgement and turned all his attention to the bowl. He hungrily ate about a quarter of it before coming to the realization that there was nothing other than a confetti of pebble-like pellets. What they lacked in flavor and texture they made up for only in a festive appearance. Meow rummaged hoping something moist and flavorful lay hidden at the bottom of the bowl. Nothing of the sort.

He glanced up at the human who was leaning against the counter nearby. The Chairman caught his eye and mroweld. The Tall One smiled. He wasn't singing heeeerekittykittykitty anymore. Meow tried again, telling him in quite a few words how much happier he would be if there were something else added to his bowl. The Human spoke in the plain voice that meant nothing else was coming. Meow, disappointed in the human, yet again, looked down at the bowl. Coming to a decision, he gave the food an exaggerated sniff, turned his back on it and stalked away.

The Tall One was talking again, this time in a softer, slightly pleading voice. Meow did not turn an ear, for he intended to make his point clear. This had gone far enough; he would not tolerate any more. Finding a place in the living room that was as far from the kitchen as possible within the confines of the house, Chairman Meow took up a position facing the corner. He would remain there, elegant and haughty, until the human came to his senses and opened up some real food. If he tried to offer that kibble again, Meow would refuse to eat. He'd rather starve than eat that pointless debris.

Just as Meow was settling into his protest, he heard a bright tinkling. He tensed at the sound. The little ringing bell always preceded the entrance of his great rival. If life in the house was, in that moment, uninspiring, and the illogical behavior of the human infuriating, then Hissyfit was the artistic flourish that rendered his misery complete. She even looked rather like a wild brushstroke.

The dainty tinkle belied the heavy, graceless manner of the old Persian. No sooner did Meow feel the vibration of her flat footfall than he smelled the salmon. He knew it had been at least an hour since she'd eaten, for that was back when he'd been stuck in the blind, but the aroma was undeniable. Lately, she'd begun to wear the scent of her food like a cologne. Her long fur caught so much refuse that it required painstaking grooming to remove all of it. Meow couldn't be sure if it was an oversight of age, simple laziness (for she'd somehow convinced the humans to do much of her grooming for her) or if the wafting aroma was a deliberate mockery aimed at him. He was inclined to think it was the latter. Though she pretended not to notice his many attempts to gain entrance into the specially cordoned area in which she was fed, they were both aware of the injustice.

Chairman Meow was agitated that she'd wandered in just in time to see his stance of protest and no doubt mar its effectiveness. He tried to look as though he were intently observing an insect. From her vantage, it was unlikely she could determine nothing was there. To further the ruse, and hopefully save some of his pride, Meow pretended to swat at the imaginary insect.

Pretending again? came a congested rumble. With a swish of his tail Meow brushed away the comment. Then he acted as though he caught the little flying whatever it was. Hissyfit was not fooled.

The only time your aim is ever that good is when you are chasing something imaginary. You will never fool me, crooked-eyes, she intoned, in a barely audible purr. Meow swished his tail again, this time more forcefully. Beyond that, he didn't grant her insult a response. Never easily put off, Hissyfit strolled closer, wafting the smells of salmon and triumph. Chairman Meow turned around slowly to face her. She stopped a few strides from him and stared, daring him to react. He growled. Slowly she advanced, antagonizing him. He hunched up and hissed. She didn't back away. Suddenly, it was too much to bear. Like a lightning strike, Meow lunged at her, snarling and wrroowling his frustration at everything. She charged forward striking out to meet his offensive. It was a wild moment of slashing and screaming. Loud, deep voices interrupted from far off and strong hands pulled them away from battle. Meow struggled for a moment but was immobilized by a firm grip on the back of his neck. The humans had intervened. He became aware of the fact that the Tall One was scolding him. As if he had been the aggressor! Meanwhile the Small One was

speaking sweetly to Hissyfit, consoling her. Just before Meow was carried off down the hall, he glimpsed Hissyfit being stroked in loving arms and attended to as if royalty. She gave him a slow wink.

In a far room, Chairman Meow was unceremoniously dumped on to the floor. Thanks to the human, he landed harder on his feet than he ought and took a second to gain his bearings. Uninjured, but irritated by this graceless arrival, he turned toward the doorway and made to leave. The Tall One blocked his path with a foot. A hard voice spoke to him, but Meow was not in the mood to hear it, so he didn't. The door shut and he was alone.

Chairman Meow did not mind solitude. The human hadn't bothered to switch on the light so the room was pleasantly dark. Generally, under such circumstances he could have fallen asleep and dreamed his way back to liberation in an endless land. Today it was not so. The room he'd been deposited in happened to be the waste place. It was all cold tile and water and nasty odor. He kept his forays into this realm as brief as possible. He stalked round the room hoping to find a fallen towel to sit upon. Since it had been the cleaning day, everything was hung tidily out of reach. He considered unraveling the tissue roll but then thought better of it. For some reason, the humans had taken to viewing him as a troublemaker. He knew he must be careful not to further this erroneous opinion, so he hunched down on the tile, close to the door and waited. Eventually it would open and he would make his escape.

Ages passed and the door opened. A sliver of light glanced across the room. He rushed to the threshold blindly and nearly collided with a large, furry mound. His eyes adjusted to the change in light just in time to see Hissyfit's wide paw strike out at him. Her claws were retracted, and it was more a defensive shove than anything aggressive. Meow sidestepped and slipped through the doorway. As he went, she gave him a deliberate sniff, and jerked her head back as if his smell were contagious and she didn't want any of it to land on her. Meow glowered. It was not his fault he'd been locked in the waste-room long enough for the odor to cling to his fur. Furthermore, it was she who really stank up the box. To be called foul-smelling by her, the very originator of the foul smells that polluted the waste-room! She who walked around with poop-locks! He was miffed.

He strode into the living room to find the reading lamps lit and wingback armchair occupied. It looked like a very cozy spot to curl up, but not having forgotten the offense at being banished to the waste-room, Meow strode over to the settee instead. From there he eyed the Tall One. His attention was far away in a book. They sat there in silence until the Small One wandered into the room carrying a giant wad of fur. She climbed into an armchair, snuggled in with a purring Hissyfit and picked up a small book. The four of them remained just so for some hours, the only movement the periodic rustle of a turning page.

Once lights were out and humans asleep, Meow perked up; in these dark hours it was his world. All competition for the favors of humans forgotten, he and Hissyfit ruled the house together. They would sniff out moths real and imagined, glance after shadows, upset vases and sharpen their claws on the thickest upholstery.

By day, they resumed their disaffected lassitude and general indifference toward the world. Their rivalry remained strong as long as the humans were involved. Meow fairly often found himself in trouble for breaking some arbitrary human rule. He was standing in the wrong place—Not the tabletop! He was sniffing the wrong food—Stay away from that toast! He was pouncing on the wrong thing—Ouch! That's my foot under the blanket! or some other such nonsense. It was a constant dance between trouble and affection. He never was sure what was coming from the humans and nearly always surprised by their reactions.

Rolling about in a sunny patch on the rug, Meow found himself particularly happy. He felt just the right amount warm, fed and undisturbed. It occurred to him then that he ought to find a way to always feel so content. As if on cue, the perpetually self-satisfied Hissyfit strolled into the room, her bell tinkling away. Well, at least he'd gotten rid of his bell, he thought, and for a moment felt even better about his situation. The humans had tried to stick him with one several times when he first arrived, but he always found a way to get rid of the thing. How Hissyfit dealt with it, he never understood. Just then, he wondered if she really didn't mind it. Because, he realized, she always got whatever she wanted. She had better food, the choice

of any lap in the room, her own heated blanket in a corner, and only occasionally was she scolded for scratching the furniture. It dawned on The Chairman then that his nemesis must have some understanding that he did not. He decided that he would watch her and uncover her secret.

It was rather boring observing Hissyfit at first. She was lazier than he and watching her sleep made him sleepy. Much of the time Meow dozed off too, only to awaken later to find her gone. He tried following her around but she was on to him. She was expert at making it appear as though he'd been harassing her when he came into a room just behind her. This brought stern words from the Tall One, and extra affection for Hissyfit. Clearly his efforts to improve his lot weren't working.

It was only by accident that he made a discovery. In the still-dark hours of morning, Meow heard a strange sound that reminded him distantly of an unhappy place. It startled him, and he gave a half-jump. The Tall One, who'd been heading down the hall just behind him, only noticed what appeared to be an unexpected stumble.

"Oh no! Are you okay, Meow?" called the human. Hearing the soft intonation, Meow paid attention. He was in the process of recovering his posture and acting as though nothing had happened, when he stopped himself. Something told him to wait. The human leaned over him and gently patted his head.

"Hey, what was that about? I hope you aren't hurt." Then the Tall One kneeled down on the floor in front of him. He gingerly reached out to touch Meow's paw. Meow, surprised by the situation, had forgotten to put his paw down and didn't realize he was holding it in mid air. The human seemed to think he was injured. A ridiculous idea, thought Chairman Meow. He couldn't imagine a world in which one could injure oneself by walking a straight line. He didn't know that humans manage to do it quite often.

The Tall One crouched down further so they were eye to eye. He spoke to Meow in a kind tone and slowly, petting him all the while, lifted him up and carried him to his lair. Normally, Meow wasn't allowed in the Tall One's lair during the dark hours. He had run of the house except for that room. The Tall One did not tolerate being woken mid-night no matter how intense the moth chase. Chairman Meow wasn't sure what to make of this change. The human climbed back into bed and tucked Meow under the covers beside him. Though he wanted to understand what exactly happened, he was being given such a nice head-scratch and spoken to so sweetly, Meow drifted off into a sleepy bliss.

The next day, both humans were particularly sweet with him. They seemed concerned.

Chairman Meow was just fine and didn't really like being treated like a kitten. He tried to make that clear by jumping to the highest perch in the dining room. However, just as he leapt, he caught a strange glance from Hissyfit. He watched her a moment too long and in doing so fumbled his landing. He didn't miss entirely, but he did have to scramble to get his dangling hind legs onto the top of the china cabinet. The cabinet creaked ever so slightly and a shifting of porcelain sounded in the room. He braced himself for scolding, for he always knew any noise from the china cabinet resulted in a scolding. Hissyfit looked pleased. Surprisingly the two humans both exclaimed, "Oh no! Meow are you okay?"

He sat back, surprised. In softer voices they both went on talking over each other, "Oh dear! You poor thing. That paw of yours must really be hurt! Can you get down? Let us help

you!" and so on. Before he realized what was happening, a chair had been pulled up alongside the cabinet, and the Tall One was balancing atop it. The porcelain rattled, and the Small One gasped. A moment later, Meow was lifted, rather awkwardly, but with care, down from the cabinet. For the rest of the day he was treated like a king. Expecting his rival to be upset by his strange new status, The Chairman was disappointed to catch her silently gloating. She quickly resumed an indifferent expression, but now he wasn't fooled.

What is amusing you? he asked.

Nothing of consequence, she replied and strode off. He followed her, not wanting to let it go at that. Things were all mixed up that day, and Meow wanted to know what she was so smug about. He batted at her tail, a definite way to get her attention. She turned casually.

So you have fooled them into thinking you are really hurt. Play it up. Enjoy the attentions while you can. She rumbled a low chuckling purr. The Chairman found her good humor suspect. She ought to be sulking.

What are you on about? he asked.

You just have to be careful, if you play that game. You let them think you're hurt or ill, and you will have an unhappy trip ahead.

What do you mean? asked Meow, growing nervous.

You've worried them. I heard them talking today. They mentioned— The Vet.

No, he said with mounting fear.

If you are lucky, they will just prick and probe you, if not … well, you will never come back.

Meow turned and dashed away, suddenly consumed by the desire to find a very inaccessible place to hide.

Go ahead and hide, they will only think you are sicker! she called after him.

Meow spent the rest of the day walking around the house, making it clear to all who cared to look that he was completely sound. He did his best to hide his trepidation, lest the fear be taken as a sign of illness. When the next day came and went without appearance of the tan plastic carrier, he began to relax.

Reflecting on the day before, The Chairman realized the experience had revealed two important things. If they thought you were hurt, the humans were especially nice. Hissyfit knew this and used it to her advantage. Now he realized just how calculated his rival had been in her behavior around the humans. She manipulated them with such subtlety that they never suspected. He marveled at this and set to work on his own plan to better his lot through cunning.

Hissyfit remained, of course, the master of this art. He'd never be able to reach her level of adoration by the humans. She was too clever and had been long established in the household by the time he arrived. Though he had no plan in particular, and usually forgot to implement whatever bit of trickery he'd thought up, there were occasions when The Chairman managed to use a false impression to his own advantage.

One fateful day, Hissyfit was in a nasty mood. Chairman Meow didn't know what governed the old thing's changeable temperament, but he knew when to avoid her. It happened that she was already in the kitchen, loitering by the food bowl, when he wandered in looking for a mid-afternoon snack. He saw her dominant stance over the bowl but ignored it, knowing that this was the common bowl and not her special salmon dish. He sidled over sniffing the air, just to be sure he was not mistaken … no whiff of salmon. Nevertheless, Hissyfit swatted and growled fiercely. He let out a yowl of surprise and stepped back. Both humans were in the kitchen, and he saw them glance toward the sound. Hissyfit, her back to them, continued to growl, unaware of the audience. The Chairman recognized his chance. He, with dramatic affectation, slinked away and cowered in the hall. The Small One came immediately to his aid. Hissyfit was scolded for a change and he was lovingly coddled for the rest of the afternoon. Dangling his head backward over a knee, enjoying a vigorous chin scratch courtesy of the Small One, he saw Hissyfit watching him warily. He gave her a slow wink.

A few more carefully exaggerated encounters near the food bowl and Chairman Meow found himself gaining favor. Some weeks after the first "assault" by Hissyfit, Meow had come to view it all as a funny game. He'd provoke her, just out of the humans' sight, and when she reacted, he'd make a sound or quick movement that drew their attention. All they would see was an angry Hissyfit, and poor Meow. Usually she didn't fall for it, but she was old and grumpy enough that he got her a few times. Finally, one particularly loud standoff between the two cats led to a fight among the humans.

The Small One became very agitated. She began to yowl much like a cat, which she usually only did if she fell down or was forced to tidy her room. The Chairman, realizing the catalyst was his own predicament, paid closer attention to human words than usual.

"He's such a good kitty and always uses the box and doesn't even shed that much and it's not fair. You don't even care!" She was claiming the Tall One's treatment of him was unjust. Interesting.

"All he ever wanted was a little bit of salmon!"

Well that's not entirely true, thought Meow.

"Not that yucky kibble!" She shouted like she'd been the one forced to eat the stuff, he marveled. "He's gonna get all skinny and sick! You can't survive on that kind of stuff. He needs Nuu-trea-ents." The small one struggled to enunciate that last word. On and on she went.

"And fat, old Hissyfit doesn't ever do what you tell her, and she's mean to poor Meow, and she still gets treated like a princess! It's NOT FAIR!" She decried Hissyfit's dominance of the house! This was world-changing. Meow couldn't believe it. Perhaps he ought to pay attention to the words of the humans more often. He did his best to look pathetic in an attempt to add credibility to the Small One's claims. She went on but the monologue became more abstract and Cat lost track of the point.

"You don't wait for starving children overseas to lose their teeth before you feed them something better than emergency rations!" This last bit didn't make any sense to The Chairman, nor did it make much sense to the other human. Coming back round again, the Small One concluded with the wailing statement, "Chairman Meow deserves salmon every day too." Sniffling a bit, she folded her arms across her chest and glared up at the Tall One. Meow, wanting to gloat, glanced around for Hissyfit but she was nowhere in sight. There was a pause and then the Tall One nodded his head and murmured something soothing to the Small One. He leaned down, scooped her up and turned to walk back down the hall. A moment later the two human voices called in chorus, "Chairman Meow! Heeerekittykit-tykittyyy!" The pop and curl of an opening can immediately followed. Meow ran back to the kitchen. It was amazing! The strange keening of the Small One had resulted in salmon for him! All for him! Gulping down mouthfuls of the delight, he swooned into mindless rapture.

One full can later, Chairman Meow paraded out of the kitchen. Hissyfit glared at him from beneath the hall table. Keeping his head and tail pointed skyward, he continued his dignified march. This day, triumph was his. She would have some real competition now.

In the living room, Meow settled into a sunny perch atop the armchair. With a mind lazy from food and contentment, he contemplated idly. Vague plans were forming. Strange and largely incomprehensible ideas flowered in his mind. Now that he could manipulate the humans, great possibilities were unfolding.

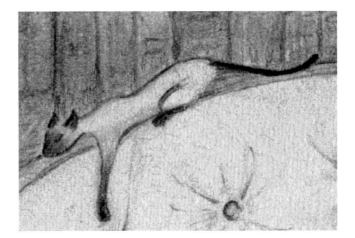

Cats Present
& Accounted For

# The Young Lords

## by Polly Brewer

They are brothers but not at all alike. I have had them since they were three months old. I was recovering from the death of dear Gordon, who had lived a long, mostly cheerful life, ever the closest to my heart. Then there were these two in a clean cage in the pet store that welcomed SPCA inhabitants, usually older animals, waiting or sleeping, not often young cats, yet here these two were in different shades of orange, my favorite color for cats. For years I have had only orange cats and here were two others in shades I hadn't had before. There they were, two young males looking brightly at me. The sign over them said, "Please don't separate us, as we are unusually close to each other." Their colors and manner sent the cupid arrow through me in an instant. At once I asked to be allowed to pick them up. The attendant was quick to take me into the area behind the cages where the little doors were open and they both came to me, wide-eyed with interest.

Actually, the smaller one was not really orange at all but an odd pale shade like champagne with huge light green almond eyes. The other had a fine white breast and feet topped by a sleek medium orange coat, not actually striped as most orangies are, but rather in patterned splotches. The pale one's fur felt stiff, not silky, more like a plush toy while the other had more usual cat hair smoothly laid on his skin.

"Oh, look at them!" I said to Don, who answered, "Don't even think about two. Remember how unfriendly Ramsay and Gordon were."

"Oh Don, these are the same age, so they will play with each other, be company, and how they will love the garden. Oh, what darlings they are. They are ours."

Polly Brewer

We didn't have the cash or required cat carriers as we hadn't really come to choose. We had just said idly, "Let's look in the pet store," since our other errands had brought us to the shopping center. All I could do was put a hold on them just like any other purchase and agree to Don's, "Well, at least let's think about it overnight."

To be sure, early the next morning at opening time there I was, carrier in hand, Don looking on with interest. I saw all the animals being fed and noticed how eagerly my two ate. In a few more minutes, paid for, they were in the carrier but, as the sign said, clearly used to each other and enjoying the other's nearness. The smaller one edged his way to the front of the carrier, licking and smelling my finger that I had stuck in through the wire, the bigger one more to the back looking not frightened but carefully observing everything. No cries or screeches from either as we drove home.

Once out of the car and into the house, I opened the cage. Instead of cowering or questioning, they both sprang out, tumbling over each other. Within seconds they found our long hall, which they began to gallop up and down, up and down, up and down with excitement at its length and their freedom. That is how I got the young lords and how they got their first taste of owning us and their space.

Since then, I have ever been their attendant, feeding them promptly with their favorite food, opening doors, rubbing them dry when they bound in from the rain, waiting on them and responding to their moods. They quickly knew and responded to each other's name. Don chose Logan for the bigger one because Logan reminded him of missed Gordon. Jamie was my choice for the pale one. Because of the many human exclamations at his unusual color, I suspect Jamie has long known he is much admired. He has retained his kitten-like friendliness and greets everyone with a cheerful little chirrup noise, expecting and getting praise. Logan all his life has been more aloof, a self-sufficient sort of fellow: large, strong, long lion nose. He, if a human, would be handsome and easy to be around–good tempered, dependable and readily pleased. Jamie is far more excitable and lively. I can't think of him as anything but a very special animal, spoiled but with a quicksilver cat charm that is irresistible.

There is a customary period of keeping young cats inside because at three or four months of age, they begin to wander and get lost. Once those few weeks passed, out they went leaping, jumping, chasing each other. Jamie was the first to experience climbing our

Polly Brewer

low guava tree from which he could easily catapult himself onto the roof. Logan quickly followed. Then they both looked at me as if I would tell them how to get back down. I told them they were on their own and soon down they were.

Early on they claimed as if their right the large garden, but to this day they use the house more as a feeding station and place to be on a rainy or cold night. They have remained close friends but have never hung out together. One usually goes one way and the other another.

A couple of years ago Logan found a second home about a block away on another street where he still enjoys a basket or chair which he obviously regards as his. I discovered his whereabouts quite by accident one day when I was walking. Our eyes met directly in surprise but it was like he was also saying, "It's nice here, isn't it, but don't worry I'll be home soon."

Knowing who lived in the house, I lost no time in telling them please not to feed the cat, he has a good home and plenty to eat. It does seem, though, he enjoys the liveliness of their full household rather than the quietness of mine, since Don's death. He always returns, amiable, butting his head against mine for a rub, jumping hard, kneading in my lap if I'm watching the evening news. He burrows deeply with his paws and then settles down to wait for his dinner. The other house and its kindly occupants seem to be part of his extended domain, his home with me not in the least abandoned.

Both animals' strong sense of going and returning underlines their independence, though of late, Jamie doesn't wander so far down the block but lounges in his yard checking his territory carefully and frequently.

Recently there was a curious incident with him. I had come to take for granted Jamie's good health and appetite so I did not feel pressure to take him for his annual checkup at the vet. I kept putting it off.

One morning I woke early with a sense of urgency to have the visit soon. The feeling was accompanied by a sense of irritation at myself for the delay. I called the vet as soon as the office opened and by good chance, there was an opening for that day.

I took it and off we went, Jamie full of his breakfast that he had eaten heartily. He was not afraid of car rides and so has his usual good-time Charly air about him. At the vet, he was alert and interested in everything. The usual questions were asked including appetite and if any area bothered him. I answered positively that, "No, I had not seen any problems and he is always fine." The vet began to check him. Jamie looked up suddenly in alarm as she handled his chest. Then he yowled in evident distress.

"Oh," said the vet, "Look, he has a big wound here and it is festering. Glad you came in today because I think I can open it up and drain without surgery."

In dismay, I said "Can't imagine how I missed it. He never gave me any sign of trouble."

She said again, "Well it's very good you came in now. We're in time."

Then I think about my earlier sense of urgency. Was that an ESP notice from my manor lord that he needed my close attention?

# House Cats and Porch Cats

by Richard Stone

Avigdar Adams

### KITTEN

No longer a youngster but petite and feminine, she remains "Kitten" to us. She came as an afterthought, part of a litter found behind a woodpile, and the only one of four not taken at the supermarket where we angled for homes. So we kept her. She has grown up to become a most attractive, charming but somewhat dangerous cat, the kind that soaks up affection then bites.

As for appearance, her underbelly and jaws are white, the rest a pearly dark gray with faint tabby markings–except for the white tips of her paws and around the eyes. Her face is more triangular than square, though not as severely as a Siamese. She is well-proportioned, of slight build. Her eyes are a mild green that blends rather than contrasts with her overall coloration. She is pleasing to the eye more than striking.

Kitten is the epitome of "curious cat," on the move at all waking hours (though, of course, that's not so many). She is in and out constantly—of rooms, closet, drawers. Twice, not realizing she was in, I've closed drawers behind her and only hours later, in passing and hearing her quiet peeps, eventually deduced her location. She did not seem upset.

Kitten is also the epitome of feline persistence. No matter how often she is removed from a perch, especially a table or a lap, she will be up again in a minute if not removed from the vicinity. She is especially lap-happy, on you whenever feasible, with sharp little claws a-kneading at your chest. She seems to enjoy being stroked, but reflexively swivels her head to nip with her razor-like teeth. Once she clamped down on my thumb, which, despite thorough disinfecting, stayed swollen and sore for several days. Now I wonder if that was an aberration or a warning.

While known to go outside for brief excursions, Kitten is primarily an inside cat, partial to sofa backs, beds and soft roosts on upper shelves. She is pretty much a loner, though her favorite game is to ambush the other cats (and sometimes us), pawing or leaping out from under a bed or behind a door as one passes. She doesn't attack, but occasionally chases: the joy seems to be in causing surprised consternation.

There are no fabulous tales to tell about Kitten. She has lived an active, well-fed, healthy life, without major incident. She enjoys our company, or at least our warm bodies, but is happy alone pursuing her solitary games of catch-the-fly, chew-the-paper, scratch-the-upholstery and (of course) snooze-for-hours. Her only peculiarity is that, when she wants special attention, for instance, to wake me up for her breakfast, she chirps a bird-like aria unlike any other sound I've heard from a cat.

So there she is: "Kitten," or sometimes "Kitters" or sometimes the inevitable "Bad Cat."

# BLACKEY

Blackey, you will not be surprised to learn, is a sleek black cat, of Siamese persuasion: small head, long legs and body. He has large ochre eyes, and—his most distinctive attribute—five-toed paws that resemble mittens. He is a 50/50 cat, spending about half his time outside but also loving domesticity, sleeping contentedly on or near the grate of the floor furnace or on a bed.

He was one of an alley-litter, destined for adoption elsewhere. But while still tiny and in our care, he managed to get himself stepped on, hard. As he lay stunned on the floor, the tromper (flushed with guilt) was heard to swear, "If you survive, we'll keep you." So four years later, here he is.

Perhaps he suffered some invisible trauma, though, because our Blackey is very odd, even for a cat. For one thing, he is fond of lap-sitting and likes to be alongside or atop one of his human companions. But, especially in his youth, if he was picked up against his liking or even jostled from his comfort spot, he would turn nasty, striking out strongly with claws extended, snapping dangerously, hissing and caterwauling ferociously. This behavior has

Avigdar Adams

moderated—he no longer seems intent on harm—but he still expresses his indignation dramatically.

He relates to the other two house cats also peculiarly. With Kaboodle, who is only a bit younger, he often takes on a parental role, curling up protectively alongside her and grooming her at length. Then suddenly he'll seize her by the neck and pin her down until she, amidst wails, is able to twist free and flee. These attacks are irregular and seemingly out of the blue. With the younger, smaller Kitten, Blackey has no real relationship at all, but (often after one of Kitten's ambushes) they will chase one another helter-skelter for a moment or so. Then . . . all signs of mutual recognition disappear till the next brief game of tag.

Blackey is a picky but voracious eater, often moving from bowl to bowl (filled, of course, with the same contents) pushing one of the other cats aside as he looks for the best deal. He has recently adopted a dog-like habit of sitting by the dinner table while we eat, waiting for scraps. Sometimes he loses patience and impulsively leaps onto the table, having to be chased with a noisy newspaper fan.

But the oddest thing about Blackey is his transformed body type. As he matured he became a very stocky and hefty cat, weighing perhaps fifteen pounds. But at the age of about four, he suddenly changed. He lost weight precipitously, dropping to little more than nine pounds, while lengthening out. He became a wretchedly bony thing. But aside from a couple of days of listlessness, he remained active and healthy-seeming. Tests at the vets revealed nothing, and eventually he stabilized at around eleven pounds. This is all mysterious, but perhaps fitting for a cat of such inconsistent temperament.

One final oddity. For maybe the last two years he has taken sole possession of a fleecy cat-toy, now utterly flattened and grimy. Several times a day he will move it from where he left it—in a corner, on the sofa, under a bed—and cradle it briefly, all the while producing unearthly utterances heard from him at no other time. The Blackey mystique is thus enhanced.

# THE CAT WHO COULDN'T

Dewey stays in the back yard. We call him a "porch cat," recognized as belonging to our household and fed regularly but not allowed inside. He is second-class, not getting the extra tidbits to eat and not eligible for health care, yet, he is faithful and present day after day. If one of us goes out back to sit in the sun, Dewey is always there saying hello and asking to be stroked. He seems more unassuming, less entitled, than the house cats, and more appreciative.

Dewey got his name by indirection. It was before he established himself as a backyard fixture, when he was still just an occasional visitor, usually to the front porch where he'd check if the porch-cat-in-residence had finished all his food. The thing was that our hero looked very much like one of the house cats, having a handsome black coat and pure white under-belly: the difference lay in his modest milk mustache instead of Kaboodle's white blaze up to her forehead. At a glance it was hard to tell which was which, and once or twice, mistaken for Kaboodle, he took the opportunity to be erroneously welcomed in. These mistakes were of brief duration and he was wise enough to leave immediately upon detection, no childish games of catch-me-if-you-can. Perhaps it was the similarity to an accepted family member, or maybe even his gentlemanly decorum, that began to earn him status beyond "scat cat," an unwelcome stray.

In any event, one day as I was leaving I found this still-not-yet-established visitor on the porch. Greeting him politely (perhaps for the first time) I said in baby-talk, "He don't have a name yet, do he?" So Dewey it was.

Eventually Dewey came to understand that if he stayed out back he had prerogatives over other strays that wandered by, and even over the house cats when they chose to go out. In the yard, he reigns supreme, hissing threateningly especially at the slinky black cat that frequently passes through. Dewey knows what he can expect and is grateful, but he never can understand why those other three cats are allowed inside and he isn't. So despite his security and the care he receives, he always thinks of himself as the cat that couldn't.

But sometimes I imagine him with his own distinctive vocation—lead singer for the rock group Dewey and the Decimals.

## THE PLAINTIVE PUSS

Kitten Kaboodle's origins are murky. As just one member of a series of mostly-black litters that showed up in our back alley some four or five years ago, why she obtained residency I can't say. It may have been just her appearance as the archetypal "Tuxedo Cat," sleek black back with snow-white paws and belly, and white blaze up to her forehead. Her whiskers are long and also white, her eyes are yellow-green and typically wide-open, constantly watchful. And there's the rub. Kaboodle is not a secure, happy cat. Despite indoor access, she has no safe haven and only limited trust in her benefactors. There is one bed and one chair where she will sleep–sometimes the better part of a day or a night–but she is never certain of unmolested rest. Her elder brother is apt to locate her and begin to groom her solicitously but (as we have seen) at any time the preening may turn into a suppressive, dominating attack which she seems inadequate to rebuff. The result is "Plaintive Call Type A."

Kaboodle is also victim of Kitten's ambushes. While these are only sorties, never followed up aggressively, Kaboodle has not figured out that if she simply stands her ground, she will be fine. Instead she panics, squeals and runs away, even away from her meal, a cat's gravest concession.

Despite her restiveness, Kaboodle is affectionate and enjoys nestling and being stroked. At such times, her companionship, bringing views of her poignantly contrasting colors, seems a great gift. Something in her binds me to her fugitive presence, a Karmic reflection I suspect of a primal fearfulness and indecisiveness I grew up with and have never completely overcome. My myth is that I was born with memory of living as a Jew under the Third Reich and have a residual core terror, powerlessness and sense of having no right to occupy space. So perhaps this is why, at 2:00 or 3:00 or 6:00 in the morning, whenever it strikes her

Gerald Brazell

as necessary to leave, I jump up in instinctive response to her second type of plaintive wail of the "I need to go out" variety. I cannot imagine what calls her to abandon warmth and comfort to venture out even into cold and rain; but such is the constitution of Kaboodle, and such is my impelling need to accommodate her.

So while Dewey "the porch cat" (not to mention Slinky Black and Champagne Loiterer who make frequent appearances in front or back yard) would do anything for invitations to come in, the ever-welcome Kaboodle spends much of her time voluntarily outside, alone. Sometimes, she perches atop the arbor or under a rose bush or often hidden from view entirely. It is always with a touch of surprise and gratitude that I espy her answering my tuneless cat-fetching whistle, trotting with feline grace towards me. Often, before reaching the steps up to the back porch, she will stop and fall onto her side. Is she nervous of the other two cats already at their meals inside? Does she want to be fed outside today? Should I carry her up the steps, or leave her alone? Is acknowledging "Yes, I'm still here and all right" all she wants to do? Her incessant hesitancies make it impossible to know, and all she'll say is "Mrow?"

# TOM

Tom, as his name implies, is an almost generic male alley cat. A red tabby alpha, he is third in a series of similar cats that have ruled our block for several years. With their bulky build and large heads, they have been an imposing dynasty. In each case, they began as interlopers raiding our porch cats' bowls, fearless and seemingly ferocious. Because my partner has an aesthetic attraction to their particular body-type, he has had the courage to encounter each, in turn, on the porch, begin to feed him and eventually befriend him. And now that he (the human) has taken up residence in our other house down the street, he has even let this Tom become a house cat who will often (but not regularly) spend long hours and sometimes whole nights indoors. "I'm under no illusion," he-the-human says, "that Tom belongs to me. But he can be awfully sweet, resting behind me on the sofa with one paw extended just touching my shoulder." Yet, of course, when Tom calls, in an unexpectedly tenor mreow, he usually receives prompt service, whether to be fed or let out.

I've been told that, when he sleeps in, Tom has a regular morning routine. He'll awaken around 6:00 and bang on the bedroom door demanding entrée. He'll rest in bed maybe a half-hour, then pawingly and vocally demand breakfast and exit. Outside he circles the front lawn, marking the property line, then begins a survey of his larger realm as yet uncharted by us. Should another of the strays—Slinky Black or Mr. Parti-color for instance—cross his path, an intense chase ensues, frequently going out of sight into backyards clear across the street. Occasionally the shrill shrieks of a cat fight can be heard, and truth to tell Tom does not always come back unscathed. With serrated ears and numerous scars, he is gradually coming to resemble the previous monarchs who we didn't name but referred to as "battle cats."

Tom does still make appearances on my porch for the sole purpose of cadging yet more food. He is inordinately well-fed already. Taken to the vet (despite my personal dictum that porch cats don't have health insurance), he was diagnosed with a full complement of feline diseases any one of which is typically fatal. He has received a few rounds of antibiotics, but the usual remedy for his occasional deep malaises is "as much as he wants to eat," which can mean two or three whole cans a day, more than double what the other cats share. This prescription has kept him going for more than a year since diagnosis.

Tom is mostly wary of humans, but he has come to trust us, at least most of the time. We conjecture he had another home at some point as he will allow us to scratch his head and rub his belly, but don't think about touching him near the tail unless you fancy a snarl and a claws-unsheathed swipe.

Tom has become an odd amalgam of domestic and feral. With his cock-of-the-walk bearing and magnificent head, he commands attention and projects a kind of majestic beauty. He rules the street and the house. He is, as I think about it, also the third orange tabby who has been part of my household, the first being Redward, my "marriage cat" of some forty years ago, followed by Leo maybe 15 years later. In truth, I have an instinctive connection with the coloration of these critters much as my partner does with the physique of Tom and his predecessors on the street. Just fate I guess.

# The Figure Or The Ground

by Richard Stone

There still is purpose in the pattern of each week.

The standing appointments to massage each other into health with hands or words

The meetings to sustain institutions with meaning invested in their names and years

Invested in their continuance

The moments shared for the sake of the sharing: we walk to La Reina de Michoacán for ice cream, this

We can do

Attendance, or attention, meant to say "your work is noticed, I notice."


But hope? Little or less.

We sing more perhaps, but who for?

The pattern of each week is no accident

Each occasion a result of thought and deed, achieving and failing.

It is the background that seems new

Not fresh but suddenly discovered.

Was Time always there, demanding, blank?

The need for a nap, a TV show, a game of cards

To inveigle Time, to make it through to another Event

Proof against Nothing.


So where to look, the figure or the ground?

Has the past passed, or does it still exist?

Does the unforeseen outdo the cherished?


As I write, the black cat comes to sit by my chair.

"Don't touch," he seems to say, "just be near."

# Survivors

# Seeking Solace

by Polly Brewer

I can give you a small, cautious meow, more like a bird squawk, when I see you, but honest, I'm only telling you I'm not a bit mean or vicious, just very wary and scared, which I have good reason to be. I have felt for some time that my vocal cords are damaged. Now I have a very bad wound near my tail. I'm so hungry and alone.

I've been on my own a lot though I'm not old. Young, in fact, probably not even a year. I don't remember being talked to much, just harsh words from a man: "damned cat, get out, you're in my way, move"–followed by a hard kick. There were plenty of punches from the man. I cowered at the sight of his hand because I knew it would be followed by a whack that hurt. Sometimes, the woman with him would say, "Poor cat," and would pet me a little, which I liked. One day, the place was empty. They were gone.

For a while I roamed around the street. I had learned early on how to catch birds and mice so I survived, though there was a hollow feeling in my stomach. I tried going to a few houses begging for water, but everyone ran me off. One day, someone grabbed me up hard by the back of my neck, so I was dangling like a helpless kitten and feeling just like one– really scared. I felt my tail curling up beneath me instead of hanging down. Talk about being humiliated!

Then I was shoved into a small box, a lid slammed down. Totally airless and dark it was. No room to stand up. Then we were off in one of those large noisy things with people in them that move about in the streets. I had long since learned to beware of them. In one, I felt sick and more scared than ever. No room for the stuff wanting to come up from my stomach except on myself. Fortunately, before it did come up, I was dumped from the box. I had no idea where I was, but I felt a need to find out. I began to look around.

Everywhere it was leafy and green, far cleaner than the street where there had been so many mice and rats and garbage cans. Still though, there were plenty of birds and houses, but most of the yards had high fences that were hard to get over. There was one where the access was easy enough–even a little low door through the fence. There were good cat smells like arrows pointing the way for me. I went through the opening very carefully.

There was one cat in the yard, but he seemed not disposed to fight me off. In fact, he was quite affable. Curious about me, he gave me a sniff, so I was quick to tell him that I meant no harm like an intruder; I was just curious about his nice place. The yard was unbelievable–large, leafy and sun-filled, with many places to hide and a deep enclosure filled with water. The other cat went over to it and took a quick lap, like he was showing me to be careful, as the water tasted funny, but it was okay to take a little drink. I went over and took several laps. So good! His lack of caution and the fact there was a woman, who often came out and talked to and petted him, was interesting. I watched them all carefully.

The other cat was not around as much, but in the early mornings the woman called them both by name. Their tails held high and waving, they came right to her and all three went inside. I guess they went to their breakfast, and here was I wanting something badly. Just seeing them go in so easily made me aware that my own stomach needed food very much. I longed to join them, but when I thought about all the kicks I'd gotten, my eyes rolled around in my head and I turned away. The woman spoke nicely to me several times, but I could not meet her gaze.

Soon though big trouble came. In the back of her house, a high fence backed up to an empty field. One night, I was in the field when I was attacked by an animal I had never seen before. Not a dog, but a creature not much bigger than myself. I saw in a flash it didn't just want to fight, but had an intent to kill and eat me. I sprang into a run with escape on my mind. The creature caught me as I raced away but not fast enough. A tremendous claw raked my hind quarters, followed by a bite. The suddenness and pain nearly knocked me over. Still, I kept going faster and faster.

I reached the nearest tree and raced up almost like I'd flown. I was high enough that the creature couldn't reach me, though it tried. Then it left. I found a low limb where I stayed all night, licking away at the blood on my leg and dozing a little. By morning, not feeling any better, I knew I needed a safe place to lie still for a while. I chose the garden with the friendly cat and the soft-voiced woman. I was hungry, but at least I knew water was within my reach.

I got there and wobbling toward the big enclosure to get a welcome drink. Awkwardly I lapped some thirstily though it hurt a lot to bend over, so I lay on my good side, but then I couldn't reach over the edge. The cat that I liked came over and nosed me like he was saying "Poor Devil." I rested in the shadows of the garden trees all day. I was starved, but knew I wasn't up to catching a bird, and even if I did, the thought of gnawing through a mass of feathers and blood that would land heavily on the stomach was unpleasant. Besides I didn't have the strength, so I just slept some more. The big opening on my back hurt a great deal.

The woman came out with my cat friend ahead like he was leading her to me. She spoke softly and said something like, "Oh, what an awful wound." As she inched closer, I squirmed away as best I could. Then she said, "Buddy, you're in bad shape; won't you let me take a look at you?" I could only squeak out a very frightened but certain, "No." She looked me straight in the eye and said clearly, "Yes, I'm going to call you Buddy. I want to help you." I understood. I liked the sound of Buddy. Easy to understand, like her voice. She went away, but in a moment she was back with two bowls that she put down near me, and then she left again. I made sure she was gone, then hobbled over to the bowls–full of cold water and good smelling bits of food that were easy to eat. I tasted carefully at first, then gobbled. It was just what I wanted. Suddenly, after I finished, it felt fine to lie back down and sleep again.

By the next day, I began to feel better and became more careful about frequently cleaning my wound. She brought out more full bowls of food and water. I was beginning to feel safe and peaceful, with my stomach not making such a fuss for nourishment. I wouldn't let her touch me, though I could see she wanted to. A few days later I'm much better from her daily offerings, but I'm still not believing or trusting in my good fortune. Everything still hurts so much. She talks to me a lot. I don't understand what she is saying though her voice comforts and eases my fear. It washes over and around me, so soothing and encouraging.

One day, while I am eating, she touches my wound with a little stick with something gooey on the end. I scream at first, but do not turn to bite her or run off. The goo actually feels good, and since she is very quick with her dab and the stick so small, I know she will not hit me with it.

I'm now wondering if I can get my nerve up to let her touch me. I have watched her so carefully, and I have never seen her make a bad move toward me. She always opens her fingers wide and her hand is up, so the lines in it show. It's a good sign.

Do I, can I, be her Buddy and friends with the other two cats? I am still very frightened and shaky at everything and in a lot of pain, yet she and the friendly cat are offering me something–maybe like belonging–I've never known that feeling before. I know now I want that very, very much.

# My Buddy

by Polly Brewer

What to do for a creature badly wounded, frightened, and needing everything from the simplest necessities of food and water to the more complicated emotional needs? Altogether, an absorbing task just to gain confidence. He must have been abused well before being wounded as he was so terrified of me that he would flee if I came near. And responded to my voice only with a swift upward gaze from downcast eyes. The saddest look I had ever seen in a cat. Clear to me that he had lost everything and he was at the end of his rope, but not yet giving himself over to dying. Instead, he sought sanctuary in my garden that had some shade, a friendly cat and me.

Jamie, the friendlier of the boys, seemed to be saying, "You poor devil, you need help." It was he who indicated the orange cat lying near the swimming pool trying unsteadily to drink from it. I had seen this newcomer here and there before for a couple of weeks, always hurrying, seemingly frightened of everything. Now he had this large wound down his thigh, by his tail, up his back that looked split open. He was skinny and his dark orange fur was dull and dirtied with matted blood. And his sad eyes, so hooded when I approached him with a quiet "I'll get you some food and a bowl of water." When I put my hand out, he cringed and started to shake, though a start was made with the water and a plate of a little fresh soft cat food. I could see he wanted them immensely, but wouldn't come near until I left. I soon called the vet telling him the problem and that there was no way to get him into a cat carrier. Vet said to dab an ointment for humans on him with a Q-tip in the hopes of at least preventing an abscess, so I tried as I brought the food. I set the platter down with one hand, and as he turned to get away from me, I used the other hand to dab him as fast as I could.

He always ate greedily, but if I extended my hand palm down he would leave his food and try to hurry away, which told me he was fearful of being struck. It helped when I put palms upward, though he trembled and moved away unsteadily. Nevertheless, I was able to quickly dab ointment on him and then leave him alone to eat. This procedure went on for several days.

I have never seen a cat so hungry, though after some meals, his skinny body was looking not so skeletal. His raw wound still extended over his back and down his leg. At least it didn't smell, which assured me it had not abscessed. I realized he needed to see the vet, yet there was no way to get him into a cat carrier. He still wouldn't let me touch him, and I really thought he'd have a heart attack from fright at being captured.

Eventually, he sniffed my fingers. Then, as I offered him food, he allowed me to put my hand lightly on his shoulder.

Irven Rule

A moment later, he arched his neck and moved his head into my hand as though he were starved for a gentle touch. An ache of my own due to the death of my husband, Don, told me how completely I understood this cat's own hunger. I put my fingers gently along his jawline to stroke him.

Then, in that moment, feeling his rough fur and his eager acceptance, I felt triumph. "You are really my Buddy," I said to him. For the first time, he looked me directly in the eye instead of giving me that hooded downcast look. He made a sound, certainly not a normal meow, but high-pitched like a squawking bird. I wondered again if his vocal cords had been damaged by the abuse he had surely received.

A few days later my friend Marcy came for a visit. Seeing a stranger made him move quickly away again, but he came readily when I called him, if Marcy stayed out of sight. As previously planned, she and I went off for two days for a welcome coast trip to escape the Fresno heat.

I was a little worried about Buddy. I told my next door neighbor about his fears and asked her to leave out food for him, if he didn't respond to her call when she fed the others.

When Marcy and I returned, my two cat boys greeted me with an, "Oh! There you are! We want our food," attitude with no worries that we'd been away as if they were expecting our return as a matter of fact. No Buddy, though I called loudly, shook the snack box hard. He did not appear the next day, nor the following.

Marcy, more pessimistic than I, said, "Polly, get ready for heartbreak, that cat's holed up to die."

"No, no, Marcy, he's healing. He's not that ill; he's got great grit to live," I said, yet the hard shaking of crunchies certainly didn't produce him. However, I continued to leave his bowls outside. They were always empty the next morning, except I knew the other cats could have done the eating. We also checked everywhere in the big yard. Maybe he was caught somewhere, I conceded, as we looked in a careful search. He most certainly was not around.

I did wonder if he, feeling better, had just taken off. Marcy left the next day. Still, no Buddy–not for breakfast or dinner. Another hot Fresno evening came. I was reading late, as I often do, near the closed screen door when I heard the strange urgent squawk that passed for Buddy's meow. An anxious yet expectant little face peered in through the screen.

"There you are," I said, much relieved as I jumped up to let him in. During my long life, I had never seen in a cat such a human-like expression of joy and relief at seeing me. If he were a dog, he'd have knocked me over in exuberance. If human, I would have been in a huge, delighted bear hug. I bent to pet him, feel his fur, silky now as he has lost his scrawny, raggedy look. Obviously, he had been eating the food put out for him. To my delight, he allowed me to pick him up and hold him close. As he looked directly into my eyes, I had that funny sense in myself that wherever he had been, he knew now he was home. So why had he vanished for two days?

Over the next week his large sore kept scabbing and breaking open to reveal no healed skin. I saw only raw red meat in need of great help beyond the ointment. The time for visiting the vet was now urgent. Marcy, back again, helped get him into the carrier. I expected an enormous fit, but oddly, he was somewhat patient, even resigned as we hurriedly drove off. Alerted to the fear problem, the vet said he wouldn't try to examine him and suggested we leave him to be sedated for treatment and shots. When we picked him up hours later, woozy but alert, he seemed peaceful, even with many stitches down his back and leg.

Now, a year later, I have three cats: Jamie, Logan and Buddy. Each a different shade of orange. Jamie and Buddy are good friends and companions. Their relationship seems very like an adoring, sometimes pesky younger brother and an affectionate, mostly tolerant older one. Logan and Buddy are more distant towards each other. Fortunately, they both seem to be okay with truce conditions.

It is Buddy, of all of them, who asks for and gets frequent pets. He turns his head this way and that, wanting my strokes along his chin and under his throat. He purrs as he looks at me directly, his face full of affection and confidence. No downcast looks, ever. His fur is glossy, except where it grows thinly near his tail. If he were human, there would be a substantial scar. He is the one who stays closest to home, seldom leaving the front or back yards and usually the first to run to greet me if I am away, even on a brief errand. Frequently he presses close with his sturdy body, lifts his head for the expected caresses. He is an animal very dear to my heart.

# Meadow: I'm Not Blind, I'm Mighty

by Toni Eames

I was terrified. Where were my mom and my siblings? What was that snorting, stamping noise? I stayed still, huddled in some soft, nice-smelling stuff and softly mewed for my mother.

Soon, a hand encircled me and lifted me up. Someone whispered words in my tiny ear and rubbed his cheek against mine. The human I knew before was harsh and pushed my family off his property into a damp, smelly shed. That man was very angry about me, but I could not understand why.

Now, caressing hands carried me some distance and presented me to another man he called his dad. They discussed the despicable person who would place a tiny blind kitten (whatever that was) in a horse stall probably in the hope it would be crushed or kicked to death. The kindly family was not about to let that happen! Although I missed the comfort of my mother's milk, I was old enough to eat on my own and was fed tasty kitten food.

For my own safety, I was kept in a large enclosure, so I couldn't wander away. No one told me kittens were supposed to be afraid of dogs, so the ability to curl up with a furry large canine body was comforting to me when the opportunity arose.

My rescuers were kind men and were concerned about my health. At first, I was scared when I was placed into a box and heard the sound of a motor. When the motor stopped, I was gently lifted onto a slippery surface and a soft-spoken woman ran her hands all over me, pronouncing me in good health except for a serious eye infection that would need treatment. Apparently, my eyes had not developed in utero and my eye sockets were infected. Then I felt a prick, which really didn't hurt, and was soothed with the explanation that I had been given vaccines for my own good.

I overheard the older man telling his son of his concern for my safety from roaming coyotes and foxes. He phoned the local SPCA, but they were overrun with healthy kittens and said a blind kitten with an eye infection had little chance of adoption. Soon, though, I didn't yet know it, my life as a beloved family member was about to begin. Upon hearing of my plight, Heather, an SPCA employee, contacted her friend Janet, who often fostered kittens that needed special care. She had the perfect solution, but some serious persuasion would be in order.

Toni, Janet's friend, had that very day euthanized the third of her four elderly cats and said she wanted another feline companion. She had specified an older cat with a well-established personality and made it clear she especially did not want a kitty with long hair … which was me! Counting on Toni's empathy, Janet asked if she could bring me over for a visit, no commitment necessary. Toni said the kitten would have to be the most outgoing feline ever before she would even consider adopting it, but she agreed.

Desperately wanting to make a good impression, I used all my feline charms. I purred; I cuddled and I encouraged Toni's two Golden Retrievers to sniff me. I clambered onto her shoulder, and she rubbed her chin along my silky face. I reached out my paw and caught the tear rolling down her cheek. Toni held me in her arms, and I could tell she was weakening. Janet offered to administer my eye medication as long as needed, and promised to re-home me if things didn't work out with Toni. Feeling instinctively drawn to this warm, caring woman, I was determined to make this my permanent forever home.

I heard people say that Toni, like me, doesn't have eyesight, but she obviously gets around quite freely, so I was annoyed with Toni's surprise at my level of independence. She should have known better. We lived in a two-story town house, and I quickly learned my way around. I moved cautiously, and when I encountered a wall or solid piece of furniture, I simply maneuvered around it carefully. Stairs were another matter, however. I could bravely climb up the long flight, but initially I was fearful of coming down. Remember, I was still relatively tiny at three months old, and I didn't like to make a move unless my feet touched the surface first. With encouragement from my new human friends, I conquered my fears and down the stairs I went.

I overheard Toni bragging about her new kitten as a feline version of Latrell, her late husband Ed's guide dog, who was still part of the household. This merry-making Golden and I seemed to think everything was a party and we were the guests of honor. Furthermore, she told friends she had fallen under my spell and could not resist my charms. Meadow, as she named me, was described as confident, playful, loving and remarkably adept about getting around the house.

I was living with Bonzie, the last of Toni's elderly rescued cats, but she wanted nothing to do with me. The dogs were nice, often grooming me until I was soaking wet, but I wished for a feline playmate. Then, my wish came true. As I mentioned, Toni was a kind person and she could not say no when a troubling phone call came on Christmas morning, about two weeks after I joined the family. Three cats needed temporary fostering after their home caught fire.

For safety reasons the three foster fire cats, as they were called, were safely installed in the den. The large one, described as calico, was very shy and spent most of the time behind the television. The one described as white was a one-person girl, and Toni was not that special person, so she hissed and spit when Toni approached. The third, an adorable young cat, was described as an orange and white male. Unlike the two older cats who were kept locked in the den, his friendly, outgoing and accepting demeanor around the dogs readily earned him house privileges.

Yancha (Japanese for "playful") became my best friend. We wrestled and chased, then fell asleep wrapped around each other. We played games and sometimes I pounced, but Yancha moved, and I landed on the carpet, not him. A blind human might feel terribly humiliated, especially in front of an audience, but I just picked myself up and casually gave my lustrous long coat a needed shine.

For someone who didn't want even one kitten, Toni was pretty excited about Yancha and me. I overheard a phone conversation where she was glowing about us. She commented that Yancha was about a month older than I. She related that Yancha was statuesque, and during the rare times he stood still, one envisioned him scheming his next mischievous move. When he was awake, he was generally in action, but he also slept long and hard. He and Meadow were so good together, she said, with the wrestling and mock fighting. She could hear that Bonzie wasn't thrilled with the kittenishness, she added, but was holding her own.

Then the foster fire cats were gone … except for Yancha. When their new owner came to take them home, it was decided that Yancha could stay with Toni. I was beyond thrilled when I overheard that conversation. I could not imagine life without my big brother. Once the fire fosters were gone, I had access to the den and could explore the room.

Still, my life did not settle down into a calm pattern. I had another visit for a medical procedure to prevent me from having kittens. At the same time, my eye sockets were cleaned out and the eyelids sewn shut. The vet explained this would prevent future infections and the need for ongoing eye treatments, something I disliked.

I woke up from a long sleep feeling groggy and disoriented, but the veterinary staff laughed at my ravenous appetite. They said I ate like a truck driver! Although I was uncomfortable, the kindness of the folks who cared for me was fantastic.

Vet Tech Lynn drove me home, and as soon as I smelled those familiar scents and heard the tail wags of my Golden pals, I knew things were back to normal. I was still a bit sore, so at first I refused to play wild wrestling and chase games with Yancha. As time went on, I recovered my strength and stamina and began investigating chairs and tables with my front paws and knocking things off shelves and counters like any sighted kitten. I used to love being picked up to cuddle, but, because I thought I might be getting eye drops, I no longer liked it. I do love having my tummy tickled, particularly when I am lying on top of my litter box, but prefer not to be picked up, as that disorients me.

Friends suggested to Toni I would probably remain a small cat, but I grew into a beautiful fluffy 8-pound girl. Intrigued with my very furry tail, folks could not imagine what it would look like if I were angry and fluffed it up; however, since I am generally a peaceful feline, I haven't had the chance to demonstrate that skill. Since I cannot look in a mirror to admire my tortoise shell beauty, I'll have to repeat what others have described to Toni. I don't know what the words stunning, gorgeous or magnificent mean, but apparently, I am multi-colored with shades of orange, tan, beige, dark brown and black with stripes on my back and down my legs.

Wishing to provide a safe outdoor environment for her cats, Toni enclosed the patio with screening. Yancha and I enjoyed going out the back door to bask in the sun on the lounge chair or dig in the dirt of the orange tree. Sometimes, just rolling on the concrete floor could be fun, and chasing bugs was a great pastime. However, one day I got confused and scampered out the front door. Toni had been feeding a mother cat and her feral kittens, planning to trap them and bring them to the nearby shelter.

In the unfamiliar front yard, unfriendly hissing cats confronted me. I did not know how to get back to Toni's calling voice. I found a safe spot away from the fierce felines and stayed in place. Latrell to the rescue! That loveable hunk of a dog was crazy about me and guided Toni directly to where I was hiding. I was so happy; I started to roll in the grass and acted like I didn't have a care in the world. I was scooped up and carried back inside to safety and, I guarantee you, I never confused the front and back doors again.

One of my favorite roles was helping guide dog puppies to become familiar with cats. Toni entertained the two Fresno guide dog puppy-raising clubs in our home, so I got to interact with lots of young Labrador and Golden Retriever pups. I never ran or hid, because I took my job seriously.

As I have heard Toni say, life does not stand still. I was now a grown cat at 14 months old and not quite so fearless. Toni had to visit a rehabilitation center in Florida, to see if extensive therapy could alleviate her back pain and thus avoid back surgery. The extended therapy didn't work and surgery was scheduled. James, a friend, came from New York to care for us animals at home while Toni was in the hospital. Having a new human friend was fun. While James brought the dogs to visit Toni in the hospital, Yancha and I lounged around the house and chased each other up and down the stairs.

Excitement was in the air the day Toni arrived home. Being the more assertive cat, Yancha rubbed himself against her legs and purred his loudest best. I felt so pleased having my world secure again that I even spent time in Toni's lap. She was recovering nicely when tragedy struck. Several days before that holiday where the television features chocolate bunnies, Toni's guide dog, Keebler, got very sick and died at home four days later. I did not know what death smelled like, so I tiptoed past the crying people to sniff Keebler. She was not breathing and her heart was not beating, and I never experienced her again.

Every time I think I'm settling down to a peaceful existence, Toni shuffles things around and messes things up. This time it was the confusion of boxes and cartons. Apparently, Toni bought a house without stairs and James would be her housemate. As my partner in blindness, Toni felt as confused and disoriented as I among the forest of boxes in the new home. However, I could sense Yancha encouraging me to follow him in a game of exploration. I had the layout of the rooms in my memory bank in no time. I have always eaten in a bowl on the kitchen floor, and as soon as I heard the clatter of the bowl, I went running down the hall to the kitchen. Of course, it was a lot easier to get around once the cartons were emptied and everything found a permanent place. Yancha and I were even presented with a large cat tree, and to everyone's amazement, I quickly and confidently learned to climb to the top for an afternoon nap.

Can't things stay the same for a while? My peace, my contentment was invaded by Aphrodite, a yappy Cockapoo dog and four new cats. I didn't know these cats; they just appeared one day, apparently family members of James. Ivory, Boots and Ebony were 12-year-old siblings rescued from the street as tiny kittens and Smokey was a four-year-old street rescue. Yancha does his share of challenging, but because these newcomers don't know I can't see them, I have become a bit pushy and hissy. I don't want them to think I am an easy mark for a sneak attack.

In the meantime, my beloved Yancha still grooms me and leads, with nudges to each new thing that comes into the house. The greatest of these is Toni's new Golden guide dog, Adora, who fits right into our animal pack and is completely cat-friendly. All I ask is please no more surprises or changes for a long time to come.

# Eulogy

Steve Norton

Steve Norton

Juliana Harris

# Gifts Such as They Are

### by Juliana Harris

It was the first day of the eleventh month, in the year 2011. A devout Hindu would recognize the date as a most auspicious occasion, and if the Hindu were a software engineer, she would revel in the elegance of such clean binary code. On that day, NASA's Jet Propulsion Laboratory, at the California Institute of Technology in Pasadena, reported the following:

> [The] Stardust spacecraft successfully completed a close flyby of asteroid Annefrank early today ... Stardust visually tracked the asteroid for 30 minutes as it flew by at a relative speed of about 7 kilometers (4 miles) per second ... Stardust's mission was to bring samples of comet dust back to Earth to help answer fundamental questions about the origins of the solar system. Apparently, the asteroid was twice as big as previously thought and shaped like a triangular prism. Preliminary analysis suggested that Annefrank might be a contact binary although other possible explanations existed for its observed shape.

Natasha was neither a coder nor a Hindu though daily she offered a plethora of half-dead moths and the occasional big kill before the feet of the elephant god. "Whoa!" Natasha muttered to herself, "That's enough NASA gibberish for a week ... must nap NOW to process … especially the part about covering four miles per second … and the triangular prism thing …" With that thought, she abandoned her warm perch atop the kitchen radio and lowered one dainty white paw onto the cold stone counter. Her nap destination was The Man's office.

A mecca of humming, buzzing warmth filled the room—hot electrical scents and dark corners packed with cords of entrapment and entanglement. As far as Natasha was concerned, the digital universe existed solely to provide heat in the form of laptops, printers, power strips, phone machines and modems. On winter mornings, she napped upon the paper shredder in direct line with early morning sun. Never once did she accidentally press the power switch and shred her magnificent feathery tail!

In official office mode, Natasha went well beyond the predictable feline behavior of sitting on Very Important Piles of Papers; that was so 20th-century. She preferred to tinker with the gleaming black plastic desk accessories and dusted all digital components with a swish-swish of her tail. Favoring the ergonomically designed keyboard, she sprawled upon its gentle wave and left cryptic messages glowing on the screen:

xxxxoooo111111111010101011111rrruuuYYttlicccc cccca;;;8nnn8;;;;, ,,,,// ///// .

There! Figure that out, NASA!

When The Man voiced complaints of long silky hair in the computer, she lifted her chin in an air of cool indifference and remained steadfast on the keyboard. The Genius Bar repeatedly told The Man about the dangers of cat hair in computers, but only those geniuses with cats truly understood his plight. On bad days, when banned from keyboard, Natasha assumed majestic command of the printer. When shooed away from that surface, she found comfort beside the power strip on the floor and oh so close to the modem with its twinkling blue light.

It was not just the digital age that attracted her, but all manner of useful inventions. While other cats flew from vacuums, food processors and coffee grinders, Natasha remained serene. She dangled a long limp paw and remained utterly still as the electric monster roared within inches of her face.

She was not the largest cat in the household, yet she was the only one who could leap seven feet to the top of the refrigerator, in one graceful arc. So keen was her kinetic awareness that she could navigate a chessboard and not move a piece in the process.

Juliana Harris

Not far from the chess table stood a large square coffee table that hosted jigsaw puzzles during dreary winter months. Raised listening to National Public Radio's *Stardate* and *Science Friday*, plus the complete works of Douglas Adams (*Long Dark Teatime of the Soul* was her all-time favorite), Natasha had developed a keen appreciation for pondering the universe's deeper questions. Her pure white catmind believed that lounging upon puzzle pieces facilitated an intuitive understanding of event horizons, gravity, time travel and black holes.

As spring tempted winter, puzzles were returned to the closet, and narcissus stood tall on the table. Natasha had a penchant for dipping a long white paw deep into the vase and lifting it to her mouth for a drippy lick. Her preference for drinking flower water led to an endless stream of tipped vases, wilted flowers, wet rugs and reprimands.

On summer days, Natasha sought refuge in The Man's vegetable garden. She slumbered beneath broad leaves of comfrey and squash and rangy thickets of catmint. At the first hint of dusk, The Man would call her name, and she would ignore him until she was ready to leave her garden lair. By the time she strolled up the path to the house, hawks had turned in for the night and owls had taken flight. The howl of coyotes might be close, but Natasha never quickened her pace; this was her land, and she reigned supreme.

A finely tuned alpha, Natasha commandeered all felines and canines who dared to cross the threshold. She maintained this balance of power with a savvy blend of lofty superiority and total disregard. At times, she co-existed with up to thirteen cats and three big dogs, yet rarely did she lash out directly—such behavior was undignified and decidedly beneath her. Those heathen interlopers and good-for-nothing strays were unworthy of her attention and, playing right into her game, none challenged her authority. Once, however; she showed a different face.

The ranch, to the east, had recently acquired a bouncy Great Dane puppy already nine hands high and bursting with big puppy personality. One morning, while Natasha was sunning on the front porch, he bounded up the steps with such exuberance that a startled Natasha rose straight up into the air like a popcorn escaping its pan. With every hair on end, she met the pup's bumbling good nature with fury. Squarely, she faced him as he regarded a Mohawk that would put a punk to shame. His hesitation at the oddity before him gave her the split second she needed to land a vicious swipe upon his tender nose. Not satisfied with inflicting injury, she rose onto her hind legs and chased the pup a good 15 feet down the path. He retreated toward his ranch tearfully yelping as blood streamed down his neck. Never before had she run upright such a distance while savagely waving her front paws in fisticuff movements. The Man called the neighbor and apologized for the damage an eight-pound kitty had inflicted on a beast roughly 40 times her size. Natasha spent the next 24 hours grooming.

Luxuriating in a fine silky coat is one thing, but incessant preening is another. All the fuss with her "do" resulted in hairballs, and Natasha was deeply offended by receiving a dab of dreadful brown paste on the tip of her paw. Who would think of sticking a fine silk ballet slipper into dog poo? Quickly, find a carpet or bedspread to wipe off every last trace of goop.

I suppose The Man and I had been remiss in hairball treatment. One fine November evening, Natasha began the preliminary cough that signaled a hairball was on the way. She went to her favorite spit-up spot—the dark blue flower in the center of the Persian rug in the foyer. Within earshot of her coughing, The Man quickly raced from his office to let her out the front door. She knew the routine well—barf on the porch and gain entry to the house later.

By nine o'clock that evening, I realized I had not seen her in a while, so I opened the door and called her name. I waited impatiently and announced to no one that I was not a doorman, and I would not stand there forever. Even so, I did stand there forever and

Juliana Harris

challenged myself to be perfectly still like a high yogi or a guard at Buckingham Palace. Finally, I abandoned the threshold and retreated.

At ten o'clock, I slipped on my down jacket and walked outside calling her name. I cast my flashlight beam high into the towering eucalyptus and oaks. Why was I looking up there? She was not a big tree climber, yet the dark side of my mind was already on high alert. Admittedly, I was searching for bits of white fluff dangling from a limb. Did an owl descend upon her and swing up high to dismember her body among the tallest branches? I admonished myself for thinking such thoughts. Nothing in the trees. Somewhat relieved, I continued to walk around the house. I took the path to the sheds and opened the doors. I walked up to the road and cast my beam up and down. Nothing. Good, I thought; she is not a victim of four wheels. She is on the land somewhere ... back to the search.

As midnight approached, I retraced my steps and fought off uneasy feelings. Natasha was 19 years old. She would not have wandered far at night. Going to bed knowing she was unaccounted for led to a fitful sleep. I woke early to a gray dawn and roamed the land in ever-widening circles—stomping down tall grasses, kicking through piles of brush. I did not call her name. I feared silence. Now, I knew without knowing.

Inside or out, Natasha could not move without leaving a trail of long silky white hair behind her. Outdoors, her silk clung to grasses, bushes, tree trunks—anything with sticky leaves or hairy stems like zinnias and tomatoes. If you knew what to look for, tracking her was simple. I saw nothing.

As the afternoon sky moved toward dusk, I pushed onward. I was desperate to find something ... anything. I wondered what I would do if I found a part of her: a bloody tail, a bare bone, a damaged paw? Would I bend down and touch with my bare hands? Would I pick up a stick and poke? Would I dig a shallow grave? How odd that I, the squeamish one, considered the hows and whats.

Yes, I think I would gently touch a little furry paw with my bare hands. I might even raise my hands to my face and breathe in deeply. I flashed back to standing in my father's closet right after he died. I had pressed my face into his starched shirts and memorized his scent. I found comfort in that closet and the sense that he was not yet entirely *gone* gone. Grisly and tender thoughts mingled as I brought myself back to the task at hand. Yes, I think I would stroke a smooth white bone even if it had a bit of gristle and blood. Yes, I would find a sturdy stick and dig a hole. I started to look for a stick.

Trudging down the narrow path and crossing over the creek, I gained insight into why people who lose loved ones at sea or war long to have a body returned. I never understood the closure idea before. Now, I know. A body stops the mind from wandering dangerously to the intersection of time and space where the sought still lives and waits ... hopefully ... hopelessly.

Walking the western fields, I realized how often death is directly in my path. In the thickly wooded forests of the northeast, I used to wonder where animals go to die. The forest teems with life, yet rarely does one stumble upon a carcass. Here, in the vast openness of the western landscape, death reveals itself as much as

Juliana Harris

life does—right out in the open, for all to see. Between the stands of eucalyptus and oaks, I find that birds do fall from the sky and simply die. They do impale themselves on long cactus needles. They do meet their fate in the talons of birds of prey.

Daily, I find at least one animal, if not two. Some days, the tally is remarkably high: a mockingbird, a scrub jay, a baby gopher snake, a vole, a ground squirrel, hundreds of barn owl feathers and unrecognizable parts. I try to find solace in accepting nature's rhythms: birth, life, death, birth ... Pondering those things made me feel uneasy, for I was just about to begin chemo and assumed I would go through treatment cuddled up with my fate and my constant companion of 19 years.

Suddenly, all life-death musings ceased as I froze in my tracks. Before me lay a small bundle of white hair. Evidence? I bent down and probed closely with a stick. A bit of gray hair mixed in with the white. Hairballs? Feces? Did a coyote eat her right here beneath the graceful arch of the mimosa tree? I glanced about for a piece of fur or bone, or signs of a struggle. Nothing. Perhaps Natasha walked along this path and left this hairball here long ago. I wanted to cry, but tears would not come.

Staring blankly into space, I surveyed the land of easy evidence and realized I would probably never find her body. I walked on preoccupied with thoughts of coyote behavior. The life of the pack depends upon its huntress. Coyotes rarely leave evidence of the kill. If it was a coyote, she was just doing her job. I realized I cannot blame the coyote, or the hawk or the owl.

After two weeks of holding back, I stood in the dry winter grasses and sobbed and shook until nothing was left. Amid the torrent of tears, I felt something shift inside me and realized I was crying not only for Natasha, but for the suspected coyote, as well! Oh, the poor misunderstood coyote! I felt a growing sense of compassion for all coyotes everywhere! If my darling ball of white fluff fed a coyote, so be it. In death, she served a purpose. As my mind raced along this path, it dawned on me that just as I cannot blame the coyote, I cannot make cancer my enemy. That day, I recognized something intangible that eased my fear of dying. Fear still lurks in the back woods of my mind, but I gained a perspective in those moments that has never left me. I survived cancer and the loss of Natasha. I realize how deeply fortunate I am to have known them both. Gifts such as they are.

In the early days of February, while sitting in quiet reflection, Natasha came to me as a changeling: a shape-shifting vision; cat/woman/bird; wearing a white gown; a kindly cat face; translucent wings; long white hair unfurling into nothingness. In this ephemeral state, she reiterated into my conscious mind that the coyote/owl/hawk is not the enemy.

Do not mourn my death ... did you not see me in the cloud formations, weeks ago?

No, Natasha, I did not. How could I have missed you?

I am always searching the sky for satellites and imagining what drama might be going on inside the space station. I have accepted the fact that I will never ride on a starship or know what life will be like 100 or 500 years from now. I've lost touch with specific news of the asteroid Annefrank, though I have learned that we are all most definitely made of stardust.

I loved you, Natasha. Still do. Always will.

# Adieu

We've done our best to introduce
Our feline friends (and foes),
The cats that won our hearts and minds
That brought us smiles and woes.

And so, dear friends, it's proper now
(If Emmaline's law prevails)
To leave for you, with fond farewell,
One final set of tails.

Juliana Harris

# One Last Tail

Juliana, Polly and Richard wish to extend our thanks to Toni Eames, Julie Harcos, Jade Livingston and Kathy Wosika for allowing us to use their material inspired by their own long associations with cats; to guest illustrators and photographers Avigdar Adams, Jade Livingston, Benjamin Locke, Irven Rule and Timothy Savage; to cover artist Karen Kozlow and graphic artist Steve Norton for permission to include their wonderful artwork.